Spring in the Mitten

A collection of writings
by
Shiawassee Area Writers

Summit Street Publishing

SPRING IN THE MITTEN
Published by Summit Street Publishing
131 West Grand River
Owosso, Michigan 48867

Copyright © 2019

ISBN 978-1-7326522-1-7

Publishing in the United States by Summit Street Publishing, Owosso, Michigan.

Cover Art: Jim Edward Hill
Cover Design: Kristy Sweers
Cover Photos: Emily E. Lawson Photography

Printed in the United States of America
2019

10 9 8 7 6 5 4 3 2 1

The *Shiawassee Area Writers* started in May 2017 to help individuals have a gathering where interaction, collaboration, finding empathy as well as joy, could be found in the process of writing and publishing.

This is the second anthology for the *Shiawassee Area Writers* group. Their first anthology was published in September 2018 and entitled, Winter in the Mitten.

Proceeds from this book will go toward local high school scholarships for seniors pursuing degrees or continued education in creative writing, literature, or journalism.

For more information, contact President/Founder Elizabeth Wehman at shiawasseeareawriters@gmail.com. Meetings are held twice a month, please visit www.shiareawriters.com for meeting dates and times.

Our *Shiawassee Area Writers* anthologies are published to give authors a chance to see their work in print. The process is extensive after submitting a possible writing for publication. It includes refining that entry to its best. Six fellow SAW members work as editors and critique the works through to the finished product you read in this book. The seven-month process is in direct correlation to what a writer might encounter with a traditional publisher.

The following quotes include some of the writer's thoughts on the process. Our group works hard to train, fine-tune, and help writers learn the in and outs of the publishing world through hands-on experiences. After publishing, a portion of the profits from the book go toward Shiawassee County scholarships to area high school seniors pursuing a degree or training in a writing career.

Here is what some one our members have to say about their time in Shiawassee Area Writers ...

"The process of editing and formatting have challenged me and helped me grow as a writer. Being a member of Shiawassee Area Writers and published in our anthologies has made me take my writing more serious." ~ *Brenda Stroub*

"I enjoyed the editing process. The advice I received from the editors gave me tools to hone my craft. The differences between my initial and final submissions were incredible." ~ *Lauren George*

"The transformation of my writings from the first draft to the finished stories resembled a clump of clay on the potter's wheel. It took time and work to get them in shape. Many hands shared in the process. SAW taught me about the craft of writing while members critiqued my writings offering wonderful suggestions."
~ L.K.Perry

"A book is never born of solitary means. It is a labor of community from cover to cover. Stellar leadership, crackerjack scriveners, and a genuine camaraderie combine to make Shiawassee Area Writers a favorite to hone my story." ~ Laurie Salisbury

"Having SAW members provide comments and edits on my piece really helped me fine tune it. Thank you SAW members for sharing your expertise!" ~ Pam McKee

"Being a member of Shiawassee Area Writers has been a great blessing to me. Each time I feel discouraged and want to quit, someone is right there to encourage me to keep moving forward. To be part of this anthology, and this group, is an honor." ~ Melissa Wardwell

Douglas Cornell

Douglas Cornell is first and foremost a storyteller. His writings include adventure stories, historical fiction, and speculative fiction. His science-fiction novel, *Plastipocalypse*, predicts a globally catastrophic end to all plastics. Doug dreams up the ideas for his stories while riding his bicycle or backpacking in the wilderness with his wife, Carol.

10-Speed Spring

Now...

I have pursued a lifetime of bicycling because I am stubborn. I'm not talking about casual "around the block" bicycling. No, I am a full-bore, lycra-clad, carbon-fiber riding bicycling addict.

Bicycling is good for my mind. Most of my daily problems are solved while pedaling. My best creative ideas have come while straining against a stiff headwind.

But this isn't a story about who I am today. It's a tale about how I got here. It's a story about a boy who discovered the joy of bicycling. Fortunately, stubbornness and a complete unwillingness to quit led me to a lifetime of pedaling into the wind and loving every minute of it.

🚲 🚲 🚲 🚲 🚲

1972...

"Doug," my mom yelled, "Your friends are here!" It was a spring-like Saturday in Michigan, and I had been in my basement bedroom, quietly assembling a Dodge Duster model car kit.

I quickly put the cap on the tube of glue and looked over the array of plastic parts spread upon my desk. This could wait until later.

I ran upstairs, pulled on a pair of sneakers and dashed outside into the cool spring sunshine.

"Whoa!" I exclaimed upon seeing three neighborhood buddies. They were sitting proudly upon brand new 10-speed bicycles.

Jimmy, the leader of our local *gang*, said, "Wanna go for a bike ride?"

Normally, there was nothing I would rather do than ride my bike. I was 13 years old and riding my banana-seat bicycle with ape-hanger handlebars was one of my favorite activities (along with playing baseball, watching TV, and assembling plastic model cars). But geesh, the guys all had new 10-speed bicycles! It was almost like they'd come to my house just to show off — because they certainly knew that I still rode a *kid's* bike.

"Hold on," I replied. I walked around the boys, each with one leg on the ground and another straddling a narrow racing saddle. "When did you get these?"

"Yesterday," Jimmy answered. "My mom took us to Cordier's Bicycle Shop and we got the last two." Jimmy and his little brother, Don, each sat upon green Schwinn Varsity 10-speeds.

"I got mine late last week," said Charles, who of the three was my favorite neighborhood buddy. He was a reliable friend, and I figured that he hadn't shown me his bike until Jimmy and Don put him up to it. The Harris brothers were very much into bullying and one-upmanship. I was a frequent mark in their little plots, and it was possible that they conspired to get these bikes just to make me feel inferior.

"Wow," I exclaimed. "Ten speeds! Center-pull brakes! How fast can you go?"

Don, the younger Harris brother, puffed his chest and answered, "Twenty miles per hour!"

"Dang," I replied. "I'm going to see if my mom'll take me to the bike shop today so I can get one!"

"Don't bother," Jimmy said with a wink and a nod to Charles and his brother. "You're out of luck. They're *all sold out.*"

Jimmy, who had been a "friend" since my arrival into the neighborhood eight years earlier, was not always honest. He delighted in playing pranks that would make me look bad in front of the gang. So when he said that the bikes were *sold out,* I had plenty of reason to doubt him.

Forgetting my friends, I rushed back inside and found my mom, who was folding clothes in the laundry room.

"Mom," I asked, "Can you take me to the bike shop to look at 10-speeds?"

My mom was a soft touch when it came to providing athletic equipment for me. She knew that if I wasn't kept busy I would probably end up in trouble. I doubted that she even knew what a 10-speed was.

She looked up from her laundry basket and answered, "I guess we can stop by on the way home from the grocery store."

Later that morning, I rushed my mom through Kroger's. Normally, I dawdled and roamed the aisles by myself, completely uninterested in helping her pick out the week's meals and cleaning supplies. But today I ran ahead of her, grabbing only one box of breakfast cereal instead of the usual three. We moved quickly down the cookie and candy aisle and made it to the check-out line with what seemed like half of our usual haul.

"Goodness!" Mom exclaimed. "I think we set some kind of record!"

Once our groceries were bagged and loaded into our car, we pulled out onto the state highway. "There's the bike shop right there!" I pointed at the building with the bright Schwinn sign and bounced with energy on the front seat of my Mom's Impala.

She pulled into the parking lot and I jumped out of the car before she had a chance to turn the engine off. I ran into the store, which was full of gleaming bikes. Most were single-speed bikes like the one I had at home in my garage. Others were British racing bikes, which had regular flat-handlebars and three speeds.

I wandered the store, looking for the 10-speeds.

"May I help you?" Asked the store clerk.

"Yes please," I replied. "I want to get a 10-speed!"

He shook his head. "Sorry, but we are totally sold out."

I hung my head in dismay. That Jimmy! For once he was telling the truth.

My mom, who had entered the store behind me, overheard our conversation. "Do you plan on getting more bikes anytime soon?"

"Sorry ma'am," he replied. "My rep said that because of the bike boom, we won't get a new shipment in until next year."

We left the store and drove home. I held back the tears as I thought about how miserable my summer would be with me riding my stupid banana-seat bike while all of my friends flew down the road on their 10-speeds.

🚲 🚲 🚲 🚲 🚲

After returning home I went back to my bedroom to continue working on my model car. My plan for the rest of the spring and summer was to avoid the neighborhood gang, thus sparing myself the shame of not having a 10-speed bike.

"Doug," My mom called to me, "Lunch is ready."

I trudged down the steps from my room to the kitchen and sat at my usual place at the table. Sitting in front of me was a baloney sandwich. A mail-order catalog sat next to my plate.

As mom busied herself at the sink, she quietly said, "Open the catalog to page 212."

I did as she ordered. It was the bicycle section of the catalog. I looked at each bike carefully, but the one that caught my eye was exactly what I was looking for: "Columbia 10-speed bicycle. Includes water bottle, cage, and pump. 27-inch wheels. Burgundy. $119.99."

It wasn't a Schwinn Varsity, but maybe it was better! It was a Columbia, which *sounded* better than Schwinn.

Mom sat down next to me. "If you want that bike we can order it as soon as you have saved enough money to pay for it yourself."

I had been promised a job mowing my neighbor's large yard for the upcoming summer. I was going to earn five dollars each time I mowed, and I'd have to mow about 25 times to get enough money to order the bike. That seemed like a lot of mowing, but I figured some weeks I could mow twice and get the money sooner.

When my dad came home from work, we sat down and agreed together that he'd order the bike as soon as I handed him the hundred and twenty dollars.

So I mowed. And I mowed. Sometimes I mowed three times in a week. My employer, Bob, was a nice man who seemed like he really appreciated my care and attention to his yard. By summer solstice, I had already earned fifty dollars. By July I had had nearly one hundred dollars in my bicycle fund, and by skipping the county fair, not going to movies, and abstaining from purchasing model cars, I saved nearly every dollar I had earned.

Near the end of August, I placed a pile of five and ten dollar bills in my father's hand as he watched a Tigers game on television.

"There it is. All of it," I explained. "For my bike."

He grunted, "Huh," and counted the money. "I'll write a check and order it today."

🚲 🚲 🚲 🚲 🚲

Over the next several weeks, I studied the description of my bike in the mail-order catalog. Would burgundy be a cool color? Twenty-seven inch wheels – that was good, because I had seen some cheap 10-speeds at the hardware store and they had stupid twenty-six inch wheels. I knew that my Columbia was going to be the neatest 10-speed around, and it was sure to arrive any day now.

One day, arriving home from school, my dad greeted me and handed me a letter.

"What's this?" I asked. Looking over the letter, I found it was from the mail-order company. It was something to do with my bike. I saw big, bold letters: **BACKORDER**.

I looked at my dad. "What does 'backorder' mean?"

"It means that you won't get your bike for a long, long time."

🚲 🚲 🚲 🚲 🚲

As an eighth grader, I was always at school. I enjoyed my classwork and had a close group of new friends but faced a difficult situation with a ninth-grader named Ron. Ron rode my school bus, and for some reason that I would never discover, he wanted to beat me up.

Maybe he needed to show his friends how tough he was, but I was the unlucky boy he decided to bully. Fortunately, I was on the middle-school wrestling team and didn't lack confidence when it came to a scuffle. I was still a scrawny kid, weighing in at 120 pounds for my wrestling meets. Ron was a bit heavier, but not much taller.

I did my best to avoid him all winter. By nature I am non-confrontational, but when someone bullied me or any of my closest friends, I would fight back.

Spring was in the air as I climbed onto the school bus for the near hour-long ride home. I looked around and was relieved to see that Ron was not on the bus. Mr. Dutcher, the bus driver, was just beginning to close the door when Ron jumped on board.

"You almost missed us," Mr. Dutcher said to him.

Ron ignored Mr. Dutcher and took the seat across the aisle from me. We hadn't traveled a mile before Ron began to taunt me and smack me on the back of the head. I ignored him and stared at a book I was trying to read. Bang! He knocked the book out of my hands. My 13-year-old muscles clenched and I pounced, putting Ron into a perfect head lock and slamming him to the floor.

"Just leave me alone!" I screamed. "Leave me alone!"

I did not hit Ron. I just held him and waited for Mr. Dutcher to break us up.

The bus screeched to a stop. Mr. Dutcher jumped out of his seat and ran back to us. He grabbed me by the shoulder and yanked me off Ron. Before Ron could climb up from the bus floor, the bus began to roll downhill.

In his haste, Mr. Dutcher had forgotten to set the parking brake!

Someone cried out, "The bus is rolling!"

Mr. Dutcher, who had been a star track athlete something like 50 years earlier, set a new record as he leaped back into the front seat and slammed on the brakes. He took a deep breath and sighed in relief, realizing that his mistake could have seriously injured a bus full of students.

"Doug! Ron!" He looked at us from the big mirror facing back towards the students. "You're both kicked off the bus for one week!"

🚲 🚲 🚲 🚲 🚲

Dad did not buy my story. He did not care that I hadn't started the fight.

"Your punishment for getting kicked off the bus is that you will not ride your new bike until the school year is over."

My beautiful burgundy Columbia 10-speed with 27-inch wheels? The one that was due to arrive *any day now*?

"You can't do that!" I yelled. "It is my bike. I earned it!" I stomped off and cried alone in my bedroom, thinking of ways that I might force my father to relent.

I spent the next several weeks avoiding him. To say I was upset would be an understatement. I would probably never forgive him for applying such a harsh punishment.

One day in early April, I arrived home from school to see a large box in the garage. It was from the mail-order company. It was my bike.

Since Dad wasn't home from work yet, I opened the box and took a look at the contents. I could see the dark red paint. Everything was wrapped in protective plastic and paper.

"What do you think you are doing?"

It was Dad. "Close it up. You are not to touch it until school is over."

I sulked back into my bedroom and slammed the door. "Just wait," I said to no one in particular. "I will ride that bike and you will *never* take it away from me again."

🚲 🚲 🚲 🚲 🚲

As springtime blossomed across Michigan, I kept out of trouble by joining the track team and working harder on schoolwork. I desperately hoped that my father would change his mind and let me have my bike.

Finally, the first week of June arrived. There were just two more days of school until summer vacation began. I had finally accepted that my dad would not alter his punishment.

That afternoon, as I was in my bedroom listening to my record collection, my dad knocked and entered the room.

"You've been on good behavior all spring. I'm proud of you. You may ride your bike to school tomorrow."

I flew out of the room yelling, "Thanks Dad!" as I ran up to the garage. I ripped the bike from the box and quickly assembled the wheels, handlebars and pedals. In less than 30 minutes I was tearing down the driveway on my burgundy Columbia 10-speed with 27-inch wheels.

🚲 🚲 🚲 🚲 🚲

It's very possible that my ride to school the next day was not actually all that remarkable. But it was the first time that I was completely free to roam about the county without any adult supervision. I rode that Columbia every chance I got that spring and summer. As I entered high school and got my driver's license, I still rode regularly. I entered some local bike races and sometimes I even won. Eventually I went off to college, but the bike came with me. I rode it across campus to my far-flung classes, and sometimes I'd ride it out into the countryside to get away from the craziness of college life. After college, I married my high school sweetheart and we joined a local bicycle touring club. She rode her new lightweight 10-speed that I'd purchased for her, and I still rode my Columbia.

I rode it because I'd earned it. I rode it because I loved it. I rode it because no one would *ever* take it away from me again.

John E. Morovitz

John E. Morovitz is an eighty-four year old retired physician who refers to himself as a "recreational writer." Much of his literary dabbling has been satirical, sometimes nonsensical poetry and essays for friends' special events. On occasion, he has composed poignant eulogies and commemorative verse. As an author with minimal formal training, he "writes as he reads," non-critically; for entertainment or to learn something.

John's only significant work is a self-published mini-biography of a much beloved industrialist and philanthropist, Mr. George Hoddy. Pending for some times, has been a family memoir that focuses on the Christian love that overcame the rampant post-war hatred of the Japanese.

These poems, herein included, would not likely have been written were it not for the encouragement and support of new-found friends at Shiawassee Area Writers. As a diversion, writing has competed with avidity for gardening, golfing, and Community Theater.

A Would Be Master Gardener's Lament

Around my home is a large hillside yard,
in which I have tried so very hard,
to grow pretty flowers and colorful trees,
all my senses to delight and please.

Naively 'twas done carefree with fun,
with some plants and seed, water, and sun.
"Miracle-Gro" on weeded tilled ground,
then *presto* great beauty round does abound.

But alack, after weeks of classroom toil,
I learned I've misused the good Lord's soil.
Woe so many are my sins of gard'ning,
Thank goodness Mom Nature's ever pard'ning.

First they made clear we don't plant in dirt,
and June's berries make a best dessert;
that wasps and hornets not only us sting,
but an end to other bad insects bring.

The P-H soil must be correct,
for any grand oak to stand erect.
Too high and the iron will not dissolve,
Then yellow chlorotic leaves will evolve.

Good soil should drain; be of a sandy loam,
but alas, not found around every home.
"Don't over till!" "Avoid compaction!"
For air, water, mineral interaction.

And though Nature's water from sky does fall,
and does so at any time at all,
it's from below that I must water,
in early morning they say I aughter.

Dioecious plants, like us need mates,
but it's up to me to find them dates.

Too, I must know which cotyledon
and herbicides each weed'll feed on.

Roots can be of tub'rous modification,
Tubers, though, of stemic codification.
The former can be tap or fibrous.
Stems, though, stolen, bulb, rhizomatous.

Fertilizers can be fast or slow,
complete or not, and cost much dough.
Micro, macro, organic or not,
care must be used when planting in pot.

Pomology, growing fruit, takes care;
bugs, drought and disease cause much despair.
While olericulture's also much work,
that fresh cheap produce is a worthwhile perk.

Each plant has preference for light of day,
For photosynthesis, Nature's way
to feed, grow, ensure species revival,
restoring O2 for our survival.

"Now you're ready," they say, "go tell and show
every one everything-how they should grow."
But alas, overwhelmed, and set to depart,
Damned if I even know where to start.

John E. Morovitz

Oh Why, Oh God

Oh why, oh God, such aggravation?
This game of golf's just pure frustration.
Each round I start with anticipation,
And end in total humiliation.

Oh why must I suffer in search of fun,
in wind, cold rain, or blazing sun?
Plodding miles with all those clubs in tow,
while being fleeced of all my dough.

And why must I know so much 'bout the game
e'en before I try-the course to tame?
Like, which of the balls for me is best,
Solid or wound, and its compression test?

And choosing clubs also drives me daft,
titanium, steel, or graphite shaft?
With heads of same, though some of wood,
Pick the right brand, I wish I could.

Then all about shots so much to learn,
to drive-pitch -chip and putt in turn.
Then rules of fairways, traps and rough,
playing the Tiger's not even that tough.

But finally to the course I go,
skill, power, and nerves of steel to show.
With dauntless stride I reach the tees,
to bring that ball and links to knees.

That damned sneering ball on ground it sits
just daring me to take my hits,
knowing full well it has no intention
to let my score be in contention.

I swing the club at dev'lish white sphere.

In galling defiance it shows no fear.
With club head speed a mere seventy-seven
it has no plan to reach for heaven.

Instead it limply leaves the tee,
and ever slicing impacts with tree.
Returning now at breakneck speed,
it hides in rough...a dirty deed.

In vain I flail with an iron club,
Then after once or twice I flub,
onto the fairway it comes to land;
A bounce or two – then rolls in sand.

With mighty swing I'm on my tush,
but ball is out...now neath a bush.
Composure's gone-anger takes its toll.
Why ever didn't I learn to bowl?

At last I reach short grass oasis,
avoiding sand surrounding those places.
The first putt is short, the next is long.
Oh why, God now is the swing so strong?

Soon comes the frightful final tally.
To win this match will take some rally.
To start with a quad's a dismal way,
Knowing there's 17 holes yet to play.

Oh why, oh God? An answer I need?
"As a penance for evil thought and deed
this hell on earth shall be your affliction.
a pathetic and hopeless golf addiction."

John E. Morovitz
Owosso Country Club 2001 Invitational

John E. Morovitz

A Mother's Day Toast

My dearest Joanne,
Of all you've meant and done for me,
The gifts of my daughters most precious be.
They are our life and earthly treasure;
an endless source of pride and pleasure.

Those words arose from deep within,
my heart that is and ever's been,
in love and grateful, dear mom and wife,
for all that we have shared in life.

'tis clear for all who know to see,
a mother you were meant to be,
Wise and caring, strong and skilled,
With so much love and patience filled.

For four little women now fully raised,
you should be proud and must be praised.
It is with loving heart I pray
for you a blessed Mother's Day.

~John

Patti Rae Fletcher

Patti Rae Fletcher discovered her passion for writing while employed in an elementary school library for eighteen years. She began her journey at the Children's Institute of Literature and graduated with three diplomas.

Besides her entries in the Shiawassee Area Writers (SAW) first seasonal anthology, *Winter in the Mitten,* she has also written for *Scholastic Book Fairs, Family, Fish,* and *Game* magazine, *Woman's World* and others. Patti is an active member of the, Society of Children's Book Writers and Illustrators, for over a decade and has served as the Vice President of the SAW group since 2017.

Fletcher's first book debuted in 2015: *This Sign Was Mine, Message Received!* A memoir where Patti realized synchronicities and extraordinary experiences in her life were actually divine signs from the Universe that brought her messages, answers, guidance, and nothing short of a few miracles.

Book two titled: *Sign's of Love, Recognize the Miracles,* is about how divine timing and paying attention to coincidence or the unusual in one's life can literally be a matter of life or death. She believes we all receive guidance and signs. Find out how to recognize your signs and be grateful for even the tiniest miracles.

Her newest publication is a creative non-fiction picture book, *Whoa Nilly, a Nymph Grows Up.*

Fletcher is a lifelong Michigander. She is married with two sons and one granddaughter and loves being outdoors. Follow Patti on Facebook, This Sign was Mine or @pattiraefletcher

The inspiration for this poem came to me one summer evening. It was the night of the Shiawassee Area Writer's (SAW) meeting to discuss the deadlines and guidelines for this book, the second in SAW's seasonal anthology series.

I had no idea what I would write about or with my recent diagnosis, surgery, and possible treatments approaching, if I would feel inspired at all.

However, as I fell asleep on this particular late summer night, I took my mind from my health situation to thoughts about spring and what would be interesting to write about. It was a dream I now refer to as the miraculous two-fer. This version with a twist.

THIS LION'S QUEST

Pondering a springtime poem, with a wide yawn
Maybe tonight I'll dream of a crocus or a fawn

My midnight muse wasn't what I had in mind
The Universe's signals must not have aligned

There stood a lion confident and proud
The breeze hoisted his mane as he bowed

Each strand shined as a silken sunlit golden thread
Face to face with this lion, would turn anyone's head

He appeared regal from his head to the ground
His stare conveyed his purpose to be profound

Expectant he stood with a fearless grin
There'd be no battle, I had no doubt he'd win

His perceptiveness high, wearing dominion and splendor
My senses vibrated with a strong urge to surrender

This lion, a sight to see had a plan to execute
He wasn't leaving without me, his newest recruit

My efforts were slow in his direction
There was comfort and a soothing connection

Tiny birds or bunnies are spring creatures I adore
Peonies and buds are things in which I have a rapport

Some landowners don't care if the lions stay or go
Others hunt to kill using poisons or other ammo

Lions are famed for fierceness, strength, and power
I'd rather write at length about a shamed wildflower

The lion's young are the fluffiest around
These soft delights attract children abound

History shows they have provided medicine fit for kings
You may ask, what does a lion have to do with such things

This dream, not about writing, but one wild discovery
Who knew this lion could assist with *my* potential recovery

My mind, body and spirit are presently on the mend
Thanks to queries I now call this lion my lifelong friend

From sprout and stem to bloom, laden with natural nutrition
This lion can aid in most any medical condition

Reduces cholesterol, purifies blood, and clears the skin
Heals urinary tract infections, I'd say it's all a win-win

Tests show he helps with digestion, and fortifies the liver
Controls sugars, stamina, and is an all around health giver

There's more... parts of this lion are memory enhancers
But the best factor... it destroys precise cells of cancers

So, if you haven't already guessed

This (Dandelion) has conquered its quest.

This dream began with a magnificent, extraordinary, vivid and detailed dandelion in the center of a field. Sounds boring, right? But it was anything but. It called, actually roared to me. I figured since I had thought about the spring entry before sleep, that this vision was for that purpose, but as I did the research I knew and felt the familiar warmth, and tingling sensations I have learned to trust as a divine sign that holds an important message. This dream was meant to help me maintain my personal health for the rest of my life. I've learned to pay attention when the Universe gives me signs.

I wrote the poem first to give the lion a mystery spin for something fun and different for this books collection. I intend to include a prose version of my dream in my upcoming book to be published in the fall of 2019, titled; *Signs of Love: Recognize the Miracles.* This is book two to my previous title; *This Sign Was Mine, Message Received!*

On a personal note: First, it's rare I remember any of my dreams and second, I have taken the message seriously and incorporated this miraculous plant, what most consider a wild weed, in the form of tea to my daily diet. Every part of the dandelion can be utilized even, the milky substance for medicinal purposes and has been for hundreds of years.

There are many healthy ways to use this wonderful plant: In teas, salads, and it's available in capsules. The greens can be eaten raw, juiced or cooked. I have heard they make a dandelion wine too.

This powerful natural healing plant helps with at least three of my health conditions and most likely a few more.

*And as always, please consult your doctor about interactions with any natural remedies, homeopathic supplements, herbs, and or oils that can interfere with your prescribed medications. Make sure they are safe for you.

I am forever grateful for the gifts, curiosity, insights, and visions that I receive from the universe.

For more information and updates on the release of my new book, *Signs of Love: Recognize the Miracles*. Please find me on Facebook, under @pattiraefletcher, or check out my website at, http:// www.pattiraefletcher.com/

For detailed information about the benefits of dandelions, check the sites below or Google dandelion health.

https://www.healthline.com/nutrition/dandelion-benefits#section1

https://www.consciouslifestylemag.com/dandelion-root-tea-health-benefits/

Maureen Bishop Gilna

Maureen Bishop Gilna has been a member of the Shiawassee Area Writers since 2017.

Having resided in Owosso and Corunna, Maureen has been active in her church and community all her life. She graduated from Owosso High School in the class of 1956.

Among her many achievements, Maureen has received many community awards of achievement throughout the years. She has been active in the Memorial Hospice Program since 1982.

Her book, *Be Not Afraid in the Presence of His Light* was published in 2013. In that book she shares the spiritual and miraculous moments of her near death experience. Her writings can also be found in the first Shiawassee Area Writer's anthology, *Winter in the Mitten*.

Maureen lives with her husband, Richard, on the family farm in Corunna. They are the parents of five children and six grandchildren.

THE OLD OAK TREES

(Granddaughter, Daughter, Sister, Wife, Daughter-in-law, Mother, Mother-in-law and Grandmother.)

Approximately 175 years ago, in the backyard of a country farm home, two little acorns decided to become trees. They grew very close together. As the years went by, they appeared to become one tree, yet they were separate. They flourished in the sunlight and rich soil and provided excellent shade during the hot summer months. They grew very tall and majestic for all to admire.

In the fall, their brilliant rust and orange leaves brought much delight to those who lived close by. They were the last trees in the farm neighborhood to let loose of those beautiful leaves which became a blanket of nourishment for the grass beneath them. The fruits of their existence dropped on the ground in the form of acorns. These acorns provided food for the wild animals well into the cold harsh winter months.

The barren oak trees stood just as majestically throughout the winter, heavily clothed with the ice and snow that fell on their branches. They were two very strong trees who refused to give up their huge branches to the elements that sought to destroy them.

Each year more branches appeared and became larger and stronger. The roots grew deeper, reaching out deep underground for many feet in all directions and were nourished by the water underneath the ground. These roots helped keep the tree firmly upright and prevented them from falling over.

These two oak trees exist today in the backyard of our 250

acre farm. They have been a joy to at least four generations of our family. Our children and their children have enjoyed playing underneath these trees, enjoying many campfires and long talks of yesteryears with the family and friends.

One of the trees is hollowed out at the base, large enough for an animal of considerable size to burrow into it for shelter. Some of the old branches finally submitted to the elements over the past several years. We had to prune it for the safety of those who still sit underneath the beautiful shade branches. I was concerned that we might have to remove the trees for safety reasons and then I remembered my father's words. "Those trees will still be standing long after you have left this earth."

Sitting under those old oak trees lately, I wondered at their endurance. Then the thought came to me, those two trees resemble generations of a family history. Two trees came together such as a man and woman come together as one through marriage. They grow together in their marriage strengthened by enduring the harsh elements of life that confront them. They are nourished by their faith in God and by all who love them and have ever loved them.

As husband and wife grow together, they produce new branches of the family. The new branches become strong and fruitful. As the couple becomes stronger in their marriage, their roots become deeper and stronger, helping to keep them firmly grounded in their life.

Each of these roots has a name and a purpose in life. Each of these roots represent those who have passed on before. These roots keep us strong with the knowledge of what we are about and who we are.

So the next time you look at a tree, don't just see a tree, but observe a symbol of your life. Let this symbol be a life you are grateful for and feel privileged to be a part of.

ANNA'S TREE

Anna's incurable physical condition caused her to be bedridden the last days of her life. She spent these days at her home with her husband. I visited Anna several days a week. She was unable to speak, but she could understand when spoken to. Anna's only connection to the outside world was through a high long narrow window about three feet above the bed in which she lay. I would like to share with you how much this lady touched my soul. She taught me patience and love of life.

Anna was able to observe a large oak tree that grew close to the house just outside her window. Daily she watched the activities of the wild birds, chipmunks and squirrels. Season after season this tree afforded her much comfort until the day she died. When Anna died, I wrote the following poem in her honor and memory.

ANNA'S TREE

As I lie here in bed, out my window I see,
A grand old oak tree as majestic as can be.
I gaze upon this wonderful tree,
Oh how its branches talk to me.

The leaves flutter as the branches part.
It tells me of comfort and gives peace to my heart.
Each spring I have watched the tiny buds form.
A miracle happens as each leaf is born.

Birds find comfort as they build their nests.
They and their offspring will find safe rest.
In the thick protection my glorious tree will provide.
Other of God's creatures soon to reside.

As the leaves begin to say their goodbye,
The colors become so bright to the eye.
When the leaves flutter to the ground in the fall,
I can only see the branches and no leaves at all.

The winter comes, my tree is laden with snow.
I look at those strong branches and then I know,
That one of these days I will be set free.
It will be then that I will be able to see
The Glorious Maker of my wonderful tree.

Helen Cole

Helen Cole was born in Nebraska, raised in Germany during World War II. She lived under the American occupation for a short time and then under the Communist Russian occupation.

In 1950, she and her brother escaped East Germany by American military train, crossing the border into West Germany and continued their voyage as American citizens to the United States. Her mom and two sisters arrived four years later. (as German citizens.)

Helen lived on two different farms and decided she would never marry a farmer, until she met a special farmer, fell in love and married him. She thought long and hard with her heart and brain, praying about it up to one hour before the wedding. Once drawn into farm life 100 percent, she became her husband's helpmate. Together, they grew their small farm and raised four children.

Helen is active in church, school and her community, volunteering her time in many organizations that are too numerous to list. She served as Burns Township treasurer for 21 years. She loved her job and the people she served.

Her hobbies include sewing, quilting, flower gardening and crafts as well as camping with 10 grandchildren and family every summer.

Helen and her husband enjoyed traveling in Europe and extensively in the United States in their later years. "I have a rich, full life and thank the Lord for all my blessings. He has guided and protected me all of my life. I thank Him for the people I love, the places I've been and all the memories I made along the way."

Helen is in the process of writing her life story for her family.

The Forgotten Picnic

Thinking about springtime, I realize I have lived through eighty-two. It seems that my overloaded brain can't think of a springtime memory. I sit and ponder in my quiet room, then realize we had many happy memories as a farm family and we laughed about them through the years.

My quiet room has been refurbished many times. It has served as our bedroom, sewing room and toy room for our ten grandchildren. Four of our grandchildren were born within six months of each other. Eight of them lived within a square mile radius of where my husband and I lived on the home farm and they were at the farm frequently. After they grew up, I turned the room into my quiet room, my library. That was fifteen years ago. I started to use it for its intended purpose mid-September, 2018, after the angels came and carried my husband Jerry's soul to heaven. It was then that I sat down and reflected on our life together. I wanted to write about our unique history for our family. I love this room. It's peaceful, and it became my refuge.

Sitting here now enfolded in my husband's cozy blanket, I am thinking of spring memories. I close my eyes as my journey takes me back. I am almost in a trance. I allow my mind to drift back through more than sixty years of memories. I am flipping the pages of an imaginary book from the back to the front. Suddenly, the pages stop turning. A 'vision' appears in front of me. At first the image is faint; a grayish veil of fog lifts and I see a family having a picnic in a field. As I look closer, I realize it's my family. I become emotional. I love this vision and I want to linger in my dream. This is more than a memory. It's an awakening of a forgotten springtime that overwhelms me. As tears form in my eyes, I realize I'm experiencing a *Godwink*. I want to share our life and our special picnic on the farm.

Our picnic in the field is on top of a hill in the second field behind the west side of the house. The first field is a pasture; black and white dairy cows are grazing lazily. A mid sixties bright blue Oldsmobile car sits nearby on the edge of a field. The field is being plowed by my husband. I get a whiff of the fresh, clean turned earth. The earth is breathing in and exhaling a pleasant earthy smell.

I serve dinner at noon; it's the main meal of the day and usually served hot. Supper hour's arrival could vary anywhere between two to three hours, depending on what was happening on the farm. Supper was a lighter meal. The meals were planned around my husband's twelve to sixteen hour work day.

On arriving at the field, the car doors fly open and our children scramble out. I unlock the trunk and raise the lid. I lift out a huge, double layered picnic basket. Our sons, Kevin and Jeff, place a brown, plaid stadium blanket on the rough, uneven ground. Our daughter, Lisa, carries a chocolate cake in an aluminum pan with a fitted lid. Thank goodness it has a lid; because before I realized it, she drops it. Marcia, our toddler, has her soft bodied, floppy-legged, baby doll with her, dragging it by one arm. The doll's hair is matted and matches Marcia's in color. Marcia's curly hair is even more fuzzy than the dolls.

The children frolic about, playing with each other and our family pet, a collie named Peggy. She is their constant companion and protector. One time, this collie snapped at me when I brushed the sand from Lisa's little sweat pants when I scooped her out of the sand box. Scaring me and my heart jumped. We adopted her from the animal shelter located on Hibbard Road. When she passed away, from old age, our children were heartbroken. We had to have another collie and they named her Peggy, also.

Out of a paper bag came Melmac dishes and real silverware that I acquired with coupons from bags of Betty Crocker Gold Medal flour. I baked bread, four loaves at a time. There was no shortage of coupons. I brought a wet dish towel for washing faces, hands, and to wipe up spills. We drank from used colored metal glasses that were given to me by my mother-in-law.

Nearby, Jerry is still on the tractor and I wave to him to come and join us. He stops the tractor and tramps across the rough field to join us.

Today, I prepared a meal of round steak baked in the oven until fork tender, mashed potatoes, gravy, corn and fresh baked bread with butter. I transport the meal in the Revere Ware pans it was cooked in. I still use some of that Revere Ware, a wedding gift from my foster mother, Mary Woodworth Schnepp.

The beverage of the day, as usual and preferred by my family, is ice-cold refreshing milk from our cows. I pasteurized and cooled the milk as directed. Fresh milk has to sit at a minimum of twenty-four hours or longer in the refrigerator to allow the cream to rise to the top. I skimmed the cream off the top. No floaters of cream are tolerated because my family won't drink it.

I saved the cream to make butter. I use the buttermilk to make pancakes. I prepared syrup using an extract called Maplelene which comes in a little, brown glass bottle. The recipe called for two cups of water, one cup of sugar, and one teaspoon of extract. I brought this concoction to a gentle boil then simmered it until it thickened.

Our picnic dessert is made from scratch called "Wacky Cake" which is popular in the sixties. My recipe for the cake came from my dear friend and neighbor, Becky Durling. I still have this fifty-year- old recipe.

The sixties were years of great stress for my husband and me. I was overwhelmed with four young children with their countless needs and all that boundless energy. I accomplished much after the children went to bed at a scheduled bedtime. I was busy with baking and cooking large meals for my family and frequently the hired help. Laundry and ironing on the farm was unending. I had a garden and would freeze and can vegetables and fruits. The grass grew faster then, or so it seemed. I did the bookkeeping and paid the bills when funds often were low. The children and I would be the 'go-for' farm machinery parts for my husband. I learned to write down exactly what I had to buy from a dealership but invariably, they would ask me something about the part that I was unable to answer. I did whatever I could to help my husband who worked incredibly long hours for our family.

I buried those memories long ago. Then God gave me a gift by restoring my buried memories through a vision. These are now my most precious memories. I realize the stresses of the sixties enriched my life and made me a stronger person and I was that city girl who was never going to marry a farmer.

Wacky Cake Recipe
Bake 350*, 50 min., 9 x 13" pan.
3 cups of flour
2 cups of sugar
1/3 cup cocoa
1 teaspoon salt
2 teaspoons soda
1/3 cup oil
2 tablespoons vinegar
2 teaspoons vanilla
2 cups water

Place all the dry ingredients in the mixing bowl, stir to mix, and make three holes into the flour. Pour the oil in one hole, the vinegar in the second hole; the last one is for vanilla. Pour two cups of water over the top and mix with the electric mixer until smooth. The cake has unnecessary 'Wacky' instructions.

Try it. It's so easy 'n good. Use your favorite icing or just sprinkle with powdered sugar another good option.

Wacky Cake brings up a never forgotten, amusing memory of

my daughter, Lisa. It makes us laugh. Whenever I made bread, cookies, pie or cakes, my children were in the habit of sitting on the countertop to watch and help me. On this particular day, Lisa sat on the countertop and watched as the beaters went round and round. At one point, she leaned over and her long straight hair, which had never been cut, fell into the mixing bowl and wound around the beaters, her head went slowly from upright to down, even with the bowl. We were in shock. She didn't cry. Quick thinking, I instantly pulled the cord out of the electric outlet and told her to not move, silly me. I loosened the beaters and removed her chocolate covered tangled hair from the beaters. We had a mess!

Our sons were often referred to as "the boys" by almost anyone who knew them. They were born thirteen months apart and were like two peas in a pod. Kevin was born in 1959 and Jeff in 1960. It turns out these boys played and worked together for 55 years to the day. Then tragedy struck our family, after Jeff's 55th birthday, when the Lord called him home.

Some very early memories of the two of them come to my mind. In the spring of 1961, we outgrew our little garage house. We called it that as it was built with the intent of turning it into a garage when we built our new house. The little house was finished with knotty pine, with an l-shaped open room and the cutest kitchen. Copper clad pans gleamed on the knotty pine walls. The bedroom was separate and became very small after Jeff was born. We had a baby bed on each side of our bed with just 10 inches or so between us and them. It was handy when our babies woke up at night, we could just reach out and pat their little (Popo) bottoms.

The builders were excavating the lot for the basement of our new house. There were all kinds of tools and equipment nearby. We wanted our sons to be safe so we placed a fence around 'the boys' sandbox. Jeff just cried and Kevin, the mischievous toddler he was, dug holes and crawled under the fence numerous times. The fence came down after the fill dirt was pushed in around the basement walls.

The house was framed in, waiting to have the doors hung and windows installed. One evening after the builders left, Kevin found a chisel and decided he wanted to 'help' by chiseling away on what was to be our front door. The door had to be replaced. If that wasn't enough, more was to come. Kevin found a screwdriver and proceeded to remove some of the soft putty from around the windows.

Another time I was giving Jeff a bath in the kitchen sink of our little garage house. The window was directly above the sink facing west. I looked out of the window and saw Kevin heading up the lane pulling his red wagon. He was on a mission to find his dad, who was in the cornfield chopping green corn to feed the cows. I called to Kevin several times, but he couldn't hear me and all I could hear were rattling wheels. I grabbed Jeff out of the sink, wrapped him in a towel and drove the car after Kevin. I was terrified he would get lost in the cornfield or worse yet, that his dad would not see him. To my relief, Kevin found his dad and followed the tractor, chopper and wagon.

Jeff was a very sweet child with big blue eyes and long dark eyelashes. He had soft curly hair. I dressed him in Kevin's blue hand-me-downs. When we went to town, we each had a boy in our arms and people would comment, "Is that a little girl? She is pretty." My husband would cringe and demand the curls be cut. I asked him, "Can we wait until his first birthday?" He grumbled but agreed reluctantly Jeff's birthday came. Janice Love, who was married to Jerry's cousin Junior, was going to do the deed. The previous year, she gave Kevin his first haircut. I begged Jerry to wait until we moved into the new house. I won again, but I knew it would be for the last time. A month later, in September, we moved into the new house and off to Love's we went. It was a sad day for me.

I will never forget when Jerry came home from the field with a bouquet of wildflowers for me. He was working the field near the woods and saw hundreds of trilliums and violets. He said he picked the trilliums because they were big and it would not take long to get a full bouquet.

Several years later, he cut a heart out of a milk filter and wrote on it, "We love you from your boys." He placed the note into an envelope that he fashioned from a brown paper towel. Brown paper towels were used to wash and dry the cow udders. I treasure my 'card.' He said to me, "I didn't have time to go to town to buy a real Valentine's Day card." He was my soul mate, my friend, my husband.

It was important to get the work done on the farm when conditions were right and the weather was agreeable. Sometimes we prayed for rain and other times we prayed for the rain to stop. The cows had to be milked, and machinery repaired and readied for the fields. During planting, bailing hay and harvesting time it meant lunch in the field. More often than not it was sandwiches of homemade bread, cookies, an apple and carrot sticks. We didn't have coolers so I took the lunch to the field and passed it to him on the tractor. We came through the hard and tough times by always working together to make our farm grow. We were a team.

One of my best memories from those early days is looking out of my south kitchen window to see my children playing in the sand box while I was baking and cooking. I can still see Jerry coming out of the red cow barn walking toward the house.

I look back through the years and see that the Lord blessed me richly. All of my long life, the Lord has watched over and protected me in countless ways that only I know.

My family and I were blessed by our times together. The memories of so long ago are sweet and precious. I am thankful for all of my farm family memories and the vision of that springtime picnic lost to me for over five decades. But more important, I did marry my farmer.

Lauren George

Lauren George has been writing for herself since childhood. She joined the Shiawassee Area Writers Group to gain insight into the complex world of publishing. What she discovered was a group of knowledgeable writers as talented as they are kindhearted. Lauren currently resides in Byron. When not writing she can be found spending time with her family, exploring nature, selling houses, or hiding behind the pages of a good book. This is her first publication.

For Papa, With Love

"In keeping with tradition, parts of this story have been embellished. Everything else is the truth. I leave the task of deciphering which is which up to you."

"We was fixin' ta get kilt." Papa's eyes gleamed with excitement as he leaned in close to me. The birds were chirping, and I could smell the soil from Papa's garden. It was the perfect spring day for lawn chairs and storytelling, especially one of Papa's stories.

Papa's real-life story was a classic rags to riches fairytale, complete with outrageous experiences our family debates the legitimacy of to this day. Papa knew how to speak like an educated man, but with me, he was always free to be himself.

"It was me, Willy and Cletus. Did I ever tell you about Cletus?" Papa asked with eyebrows raised. I had heard about Cletus, my Papa's brother, plenty of times. It was said that he could make metal spoons crumble like paper with nothing but his eyes.

"You got his eyes, you little black-eyed gypsy," he teased me.

My ego never grew tired of hearing how I had inherited the eyes of a superhuman.

Papa reached up and rubbed the stubble on his chin. "I bet that's how come you have all them dreams."

My favorite thing about Papa, aside from his storytelling, was his open mind especially when it came to things of a mystical nature. He taught us to believe that everyone has a sixth sense and the ability to use it, but as a society we have either forgotten how to use it or been taught that it doesn't exist. It was well known throughout the family that Uncle Cletus could correctly predict the future, read your mind, and perform telekinesis. The family placed a great deal of emphasis on the power residing in Uncle Cletus's eyes and considered him living proof that ESP was real. As such, when I began to have precognitive dreams in my early childhood, everyone was quick to believe them. Maybe there was something to be said about inheriting Uncle Cletus's magic eyes.

Papa continued with the story, "There were only two ways to make money during the Great Depression, runnin' shine and sellin' hooch."

The thought of my sweet, old Papa doing anything even remotely illegal forced a giggle out of me.

He smiled and leaned back in his chair. "We were doing both. Twelve brothers and sisters was a lot of mouths to feed. Cletus didn't want to go out on a run that night. Said he had a bad feelin'. We shoulda known to listen to him, but we needed money."

"I couldn'ta been more than ten. I was doin' the drivin'…barely," Chuckled Papa, or as his brothers called him, Bobbie.

Bobbie squeezed the steering wheel of the old pickup, craning his neck as he attempted to see over the hood. He was grateful for the full moon; at least it was helping him dodge the potholes. Sort of.

"Damn it, Bobbie!" Cletus scolded. "You don't want to go bustin' no wheel off."

It wasn't like Cletus to cuss. Bobbie knew he meant business. He pushed the brake with his left foot and eased up on the gas with his right, slowing the truck to a crawl.

Cletus sat beside Bobbie, with a bat between his knees. He scanned the woods as they bobbed along the deep Appalachian Mountain trail. "Eyes on the road." He cocked his head towards the windshield.

Bobbie swerved to the right, narrowly missing another pothole, but rattling the bottles of shine they transported in the back.

"Easy now Bobbie." Willy coached from the bed of the pickup. He was the oldest and biggest of the brothers and the most relaxed. He was breathing through a cigarette while steadying the bottles of shine with his right arm, legs dangling off the back.

"My gut don't like it." Cletus whispered to Bobbie. "I feel like somethin' bad's gonna happen."

Bobbie's palms started to sweat. The last time Cletus had a bad feeling, the boys had been out fishing. At Cletus's insistence, they returned home only to find their house on fire. Mamma and baby brother Jeb were trapped inside. Both suffered third degree burns. Baby Jeb died the next day. Mamma fought for three days before giving up the ghost.

Bam! Bam! Bam! Willy startled them, banging his hands on the roof. "That's it Bobbie! See the lights?"

Bobbie could see lanterns swinging in the distance.

"Don't get too close," Cletus warned. "Steer her off." Cletus pointed to the left of the trail, about twenty or so feet from the other men. "Right here."

Bobbie came to a stop with the front of the truck aimed toward the mountain's edge. He snuck a peek over Cletus's shoulder. There were too many men. Bobbie had run shine with Cletus and Willy many times, but he had never seen so many men come to a trade. His stomach turned. Cletus's words echoed in his mind. Maybe the men were going to rob them. Or worse yet, maybe they were cops. Bobbie swallowed hard.

Cletus opened his door and turned towards Bobbie, "You stay put. Keep 'er idle' and be ready to go when I say so." He looked at Bobbie with a sternness. "You understand?"

"Yes." Bobbie knew his eyes were wide with fear.

Cletus, satisfied with Bobbie's response, hopped out of the truck. Swinging the bat over his shoulders, he left the door open.

Willy jumped off the back and grabbed another bat. He slung it over his shoulder, just as Cletus had done, and swaggered over to the men. "Seems like an awful large turnout for exchanging bottles and bills, don't it George?" He tossed his smoke toward one of them.

The man Willy called George was dressed proper as Pa would have said. Slacks, matching jacket and a gentleman's hat. The man did not speak, instead he put his fingers in his mouth and whistled an ear-piercing whistle.

Lights flickered in the rearview mirror. Bobbie hung out the window, craning his neck to see what they belonged to. Another group of men, in a pickup, crept through the woods from the trail behind, blocking them in. There would be no getting the truck out now.

"They put the sneak on us!" Bobbie hollered to Willy.

Willy charged the man named George, but George was prepared. Bobbie watched in horror as he pulled a pistol from beneath his jacket. With darkness in his eyes, he aimed it at Willy.

Willy, always quick to react, brought his bat around like Babe Ruth. With a "smack," he knocked the gun from George's hand, clear into the night. Cletus and Willy turned and ran. Willy jumped onto the bed of the pickup yelling, "Go, Bobbie! Go!"

Cletus dove into the passenger seat, also yelling for Bobbie to *GO.* However, with both sides of the road blocked, Bobbie had no idea where he was supposed to *GO* to.

"Down the hill!" Cletus yelled, seeming to read Bobbie's mind.

Bobbie swallowed hard and slammed his foot on the gas. The truck rocketed over the side of the mountain. Time seemed to stand still, and sound disappeared. The truck shook violently. Bobbie tried to brace himself with the steering wheel, but he couldn't stop his knees from buckling to his ears. Cletus, with nothing to grab onto, was tossed to and fro. Bobbie couldn't bear to think of Willy.

With each new bounce and shutter, Bobbie waited for one of the wheels to fall off. He tried his best to steer the truck down the mountain as they narrowly missed trees. He could feel the truck sliding, more than rolling down the hill, dragging rocks and loose dirt along with them. That was when his hearing returned. Unfortunately.

"They're shootin' at us!" Willy screamed.

For a moment, Bobbie just felt relieved that Willy was alright.

Until he heard the bullets whizzing past them. With a ping they bounced off the side of the truck. The steering wheel shuddered in Bobbie's hands. He struggled to keep them going straight, feeling the rear end starting to turn.

"Steady Bobbie! Steady!" Willy hollered.

Bobbie counter steered, causing the truck to fishtail out of control. Cletus and Willy both started to yell, but not Bobbie. Bobbie did something he hadn't done in a very long time. He squeezed his eyes tight and prayed.

"Dear Lord, I'll never do nothing so foolish. Not *ever*! If you'll just see us through this, just this one time. Please Lord!"

Bam!

Bobbie felt what he thought was the side of the truck hitting a tree. He waited for the truck to start rolling. He waited for Willy to fly out of the back. He waited for Cletus to smash into him. He waited. But it never happened. Instead, the truck straightened back out after hitting the tree, preventing them from flipping over. Bobbie breathed a sigh of relief and after a few minutes he opened his eyes. The mountain was starting to flatten out.

Cletus started laughing. "By God! We made it!"

Bobbie stared at Cletus in disbelief. He started to smile. His smile turned into laughter. The laughter slowly faded into tears of relief.

Willy slammed his fists down on the top of the truck and hollered, "Wooo'eeeee! Hot dam! We made it boys!"

Bobbie felt sick with adrenaline. He wiped his tears with the back of his hand and said, "I do believe I see a trail, Cletus."

"Well, God was listening that day, 'cause we made it clean down that mountain. We ended up barrelin' out on an old two-track, led us straight back home. Willy had to break the news to Pa about the shine and all the bottles we lost. Pa wasn't too happy 'bout it, but he was thankful we survived. He did ask after that George fella, and how Willy come to do business with him. Willy neva' did come clean about how he knew George and we neva' did find out what George and those men were plannin'."

He paused for a moment and took a sip of water. He rolled it around his mouth, swallowed and leaned towards me. With a seriousness to his face he said, "We did decide, however, that the next time someone with Gypsy eyes bids you a warning, it's best to listen."

Papa sat silent for a moment studying my reaction. I felt a smile creep onto my face. Papa smiled back and we joined each other in laughter. "Whew," he said with exaggerated exhaustion, "I'm gonna give myself a heart attack, I keep on like that."

"You'll be fine." I smiled at him.

"Oh yeah, and how can you be so sure?"

"Cuz I dreamed it," I said. "You're not going to die until after I have my first baby."

"That right?" he asked with a smile and a pat to my head.

I had my first child when I was 29-years-old. Papa was well into his eighties and dementia had started to set in. He was fortunate enough to have a clear mind the first day he held my son.

"He's a fine boy," he said to me. "He's a fine boy, indeed."

A few months before my son's first birthday, I received a call from Papa's nursing home. They said he was in a mood and demanding that I come see him. When I got to the nursing home, Papa was lying in bed.

"What's going on around here. You givin' people hell?" I teased him.

"I broke my glasses," he replied

"Well, that's okay," I assured him, "that's no reason to be making such a fuss. I'll take them with me and get them fixed. I can bring them back up tomorrow. You'll be good as new."

He smiled at me with a twinkle in his eyes I hadn't seen in a while. I realized it had all been a ploy. What he really wanted was a visit.

"I won't be needing them. Just stay and talk with me for a bit."

It was rare for Papa to have "good days," when he seemed free of dementia and could hold good conversation. Treasuring the moment, I stayed as long as I could. I gave him a big hug and a kiss before I left, promising to return with his glasses.

"I won't be needing my glasses you know. You were right," he said as I turned to leave.

"Right about what?" I asked.

"About me dyin' after you had your first baby."

"Don't be silly, you're not dying." In my heart I knew different, but instead I said, "I'll see you tomorrow."

The next day my mom and her brother arrived from the airport. The nursing home had called to inform us that Papa was in hospice. I rushed in as soon as I heard (with his glasses in my purse) and stayed by his bedside until his last breath. It was a beautiful spring day when I helped carry his casket to its final resting place.

There are many nights when I dream of Papa. In my dreams I can hug him, and when I do, I can smell his Old Spice and feel the stubble of his beard against my cheek. When I wake, I am grateful I inherited my Uncle Cletus's magic eyes and I am hopeful that I will see Papa again.

Tracey Bannister

Tracey Bannister works as a Mass Communication Specialist in the U.S. Navy. She has published works online and in newsprint covering events for the Navy including exercises in the Baltic Sea, Japan and Pearl Harbor. She graduated with a Bachelor's degree in Journalism and Mass Communication at Ashford University and also received a Bachelor's degree in Business Administration from Central Michigan University. She joined the Shiawassee Area Writers Group to help with her aspirations of working as an editor and eventually to write about her passions including true crime stories, military experiences, and her love of the outdoors. She is a native of Midland, Mich. and currently resides in Owosso, Mich. You can read more works from this author at http://dreamcatcher.pressfolios.com/

The Easter Cross

Our churchyard on Easter Sunday was filled with children anticipating the Easter egg hunt or the Easter party. It was a bright sunshiny day and the weather was warm. I can remember the sun glimmering through the treetops of the cemetery behind the church. It felt good to be outdoors. All the younger children had their Easter baskets ready and soon they were running and snatching up brightly colored Easter eggs on the back lawn. The older children watched for a while and then headed to the basement where the church held all the large get-togethers. The church parties were always a lot of fun with carnival type games and different treats offered like cookies and candy. I really looked forward to them.

In the basement, there were three folding tables set up on one side with one person sitting at each table. Each person was handing out something special for Easter. This year, they had made goody bags for the older kids, and I stood in line patiently waiting to be given mine. I was closer to the back of the line and I caught a glimpse of some of the items being handed out.

That's when I saw it - the most beautiful crocheted cross with different colors outlining the edges and a tassel at the bottom. The colors of pink, blue, yellow and green were magnificent. I couldn't wait to get my own. But, they also had crosses outlined in single colors and by the time I got to front to take my goody bag, the pretty crosses with all the colors had been given out.

I tried to hide my disappointment when they handed me my bag with the blue outlined cross, but a tear started to fall. I tried to convince myself that since blue was my favorite color, I should be happy with the item given to me, but that wasn't working either. The party assistant noticed my tears and came to ask what was wrong. I felt so selfish. I told her that I had so hoped to get the cross with the many colors.

Just then, a young man turned to me and bent down. Quietly he said, "I got one of the bags with the cross you wanted. I can trade you bags if you'd like?" Again, I felt so selfish for wanting a material item. This was not what Easter was about. No, the lesson was about unselfishness. But, I just had to have that pretty cross.

I was a little too choked up to speak so I just looked up at him and nodded. The tears were still falling, but instead of sad tears, they were now tears of joy and disbelief that someone would make the sacrifice just to help me.

That small act of kindness, of selflessness, has remained with me to this day. I still have that beautiful crocheted cross of many colors. I take it out often to admire it. It was a small gesture, but that small sacrifice has carried with it the knowledge that one simple act of kindness may not mean much to the person giving but may mean the world to the person receiving. It also holds the remembrance of the bigger sacrifice and selflessness that Jesus made for us on his cross. I will never forget.

Everywhere You Go
~ *In loving memory of Helen Lee Wellman (Brown), 1922-2015* ~

The flags and photos up on your door
Showed visitors within sight
The soldiers and sailors you held so dear
And prayed for every night

As I gazed at all these pictures
And the postcards that I sent
Of all the views I'd seen
And all the places that I went

She looked at me with a twinkle in her eye
And said "I wished I could've been there"
I answered softly, "You were always with me
I took you everywhere."

You were with me at my Boot Camp
When I thought I might not make it
But I knew I couldn't let you down
I knew I couldn't quit

Floating on the Baltic Sea
Watching the waves roll by
The moonlight danced upon the water
As we looked up in the sky

Along the beaches in Hawaii
As the waves came crashing in
I didn't feel alone
'cause you were with me then

Now you're gone and I feel lost

I'm not sure what to do
There's no more pictures, no more postcards
That I can send to you

But every spring I gaze outdoors
At the pretty purple flowers
The ones you always loved so much
That bloomed after the spring showers

And I hear your voice within me
Saying "Child, don't you know?
That I am always with you
Everywhere you go."

Spring Warning

The pesky squirrels
have left their den
With their feet a pitter patter

Spring is near
Is what I hear
As their voices chitter chatter

Don't get too close
Just go away
Your dog is in my bubble

My fluffy tail
Is my warning sign
That I can cause big trouble.

L.K. Perry

L.K.Perry currently lives in Swartz Creek, Michigan where she grew up. Perry is an active member of Swartz Creek United Methodist church. She has committed to a four year discipleship class. Perry moved back to her childhood city in 2014 to help her brother take care of their aging mother.

She has three granddaughters who live in various places in the state. Perry visits them as often as she can. Her youngest still resides with her parents near the Grand Rapids area. Her oldest attends Wayne State University in Detroit. Her middle granddaughter lives in Port Huron. Perry has an Associate's Degree in Liberal Arts received with honors, Phi Theta Kappa. Her studies included Literature, Poetry, Creative Writing, and Language.

Evergreen in the anthology *Winter in the Mitten* compiled by Shiawassee Area Writers (SAW) is Perry's first published memoir. Perry has been a member of SAW for two years. You can find more writings by this author on lkperry.com and email her from this site.

MY SWEET PEA

April 25th, 1970 would change my life forever. It emerged like any other spring day in Michigan. Tulips broke through the snow-covered ground. Tiny buds peeked out of the tree branches. The sun rose higher in the sky with the promise of warmer days.

As my mother drove me to the hospital, I peered out the passenger window. Patches of snow still lay in the fields. It didn't feel like spring. The last eight-and-a-half-months had been quite an experience for me.

I remembered the day my doctor called, and mom answered the phone. He said, "Congratulations, Grandma." The news caught her off guard. I hadn't introduced her to my boyfriend. She didn't know I had one. I had a lot to explain. The doctor's report made her very unhappy with me.

Even though I worked and had my own apartment, she didn't believe that I could be a good mother. I didn't know if I could be either, but one thing I did know - no one would take this baby from me. I said, "No abortion or adoption." There would be no guarantee that my child would get good parents. I wouldn't be able to know. I would imagine the worst. I couldn't bear the thought of it.

The father of my child proposed. He thought it would be great to be married. He couldn't wait to have a wife to tend to all his needs. I cried.

Marriage and motherhood had been things I never wanted. I had seen to many negative things in regards to them.

My carelessness changed my destiny. My sadness toward the marriage proposal and my friends' anger at my baby's father caused him to change his mind about marriage.

I worked overtime to pay for my medical care and to get things that I needed for my baby. My Aunt Dorothy had a baby shower for me. The fact that she didn't judge me touched my heart.

I had been through a lot. Mom had accepted the situation and looked forward to the arrival of her first grandchild. We didn't know if I would have a boy or girl. They didn't do ultrasounds.

As we approached the hospital, I thought about our original plans for this Saturday. My extended family dip for smelt on the AuSable River every year. We would rent cabins for the weekend, and catch the little fish. Afterwards we cleaned, cooked, and ate them. At night, seated around a bonfire on the beach, we shared stories and laughter. I would miss this year's event.

My water broke around nine in the morning. By two o'clock in the afternoon, my labor pains began to build along with Mom's anxiety. She looked scared to death for me. I gave her permission to wait in another room.

I heard a conversation between two female nurses outside my room. They felt sorry for me because no one stayed with me. Then, I heard one say, "Stupid girl. What is wrong with these girls nowadays?"

I would be twenty next month. I could handle this alone and preferred it that way.

The hospital had separate labor rooms for each woman. I heard the cries and screams of other moms-to-be, but I couldn't see them. Soon, my groans blended in with the rest of them. I rolled my head until my long hair formed a giant ball at the base of my neck.

A male nurse passed in the hall and decided to stop to console me. As he patted my hand, he said, "There, there. I know what you're going through." How could he know?

He timed my contractions. He left to find the nurse assigned to me. When he came back with her, she checked me again. My cervix had dilated from a three to ten in a matter of minutes. They rushed me to a delivery room. Back then, everything didn't happen in the same room. We didn't have epidurals either.

They sat me up on the bed and put a shot in my back. The saddle block took at once. They wanted me to slide off the bed onto the delivery table, but I couldn't move the bottom half of my body. The shot had paralyzed me for a period of time. This made it impossible for me to push in the natural process of delivery. The doctor had to use forceps to help my beautiful little girl enter this world at 4:51 pm.

My grandmother surprised me. I thought she had gone up north with the rest of the family. When she saw my little girl, she said she looked like she had been in a fight. Her nose was smashed to the side, and she had a big bump on her head. Grandma called her our little prize fighter. Grandma found her to be adorable but a bit of an ugly duckling with her bruises.

The nurses didn't agree. They claimed that they had never seen a more beautiful baby. They loved her long, dark brown hair. They rocked her in their arms and cooed endearments to her as I waited to hold her.

I'll never forget the first time I held her. I studied her sweet face to see who she looked like. Her tiny fingers were so long. Would she be a pianist, someday? I held her tiny feet in my hand and breathed in her scent. I kissed her soft skin. This baby, perfect in every way, made me wonder how I had never wanted children.

I named her Elizabeth May. I chose the name based on the definitions in my babies names book. It defined Elizabeth as, a gift from God and May as great. In addition, I liked the flexibility of many nicknames. I chose Lisa because I didn't know anyone else that used it.

We left the hospital two days later to find it sunny and warm outside. The patches of snow had disappeared. Spring had arrived. My April baby resembled her month's flower, the Sweet Pea, which means 'brings blissful pleasure.'

As a mother for the first time, I had changed. The dress that I packed to wear home, didn't fit over my wider hips. The responsibility of this child brought me an anxiety that I had never experienced before. For the first time in my life, I had a fear of storms. I had a little one to protect. I loved her more than anyone. My emotions ran high and low.

More than anything, I felt thankful to God for this precious gift. What a wonderful surprise to discover that the plan for me included motherhood. God knew my sweet pea would bring me joy and give my life a special purpose.

SPRING BLOSSOMS

The desire for wedded bliss began to blossom in my sweet pea's heart. How would I help my beautiful girl plan her May 1993 wedding? As a single mom disappointed in love, I had not turned out to be the good mother that I had hoped to be.

Lisa met Andy in 1984 at a Christmas party hosted by my aunt and uncle. A few weeks after the party, Lisa and Andy were invited back to their home to hang out with her cousins.

As I dropped Lisa off, I noticed a couple of kids on snowmobiles as they raced through the fields. I thought I should go back and tell Lisa to wear a helmet if she got on the snow-machine. I shrugged it off, because she had been scared to ride one before. Lisa would never get on a snowmobile.

Not only did she get on it, but she decided to drive it with Andy seated behind her. I guess she wanted to impress him. I don't know if she drove it out into the field, but she did drive it in a backyard, where she crashed into a cement birdbath. The concrete basin came off the stand and flew up in the air. It missed her eye. The deep cut over her brow required plastic surgery. Andy waited with her at the hospital during surgery and recovery. Within a few weeks, he became her boyfriend.

When Lisa turned sixteen, I moved to a city an hour away. I had very little contact with her for two years. She stayed with my mother.

Lisa and Andy dated all through high school. Born on the same day, a year apart, they celebrated their birthdays. They enjoyed their proms and worked at various jobs while in school.

I moved back near Lisa when she graduated. After graduation, she moved out of the area. Better job opportunities were available in her new location. I did see her more than before, but still not a lot.

Four years later, Lisa and Andy decided to get married in a beautiful church near home. I put a hundred dollars down to hold it for the date they had chosen.

Next, she chose the Ramada Inn for her reception. I went with her to make the dinner and reception plans. We went to bridal shows, bought bride magazines, shopped and dined out a lot. I couldn't have been happier for her and for me. I felt blessed to be included. She forgave my sins and weaknesses with grace.

Their wedding took eighteen months to plan. Lisa and Andy paid for most of their wedding with a little help from family.

I don't know what it feels like to be a bride, but I can tell you as a mother of the bride, my heart filled with joy and anticipation as we planned for the big day.

Lisa had connected with her father and his family in the two years of my absence. Her five bridesmaids included her two half sisters. Her father would walk her down the aisle and give her away.

Lisa and I waited in a beautiful room papered with pink roses, for him to come get her. We looked in the gold framed full length mirror at each other as the photographer snapped our picture. I couldn't take my eyes off her in her wedding gown and veil, as she held a spring bouquet of hot pink roses, white calla lilies and baby's breath, purple hyacinth, and a long trail of teal ivy.

Her father arrived and he couldn't take his eyes off her either. My uncle escorted me to my seat. The music began and the girls in their pink, purple, and teal dresses with matching bouquets proceeded down the aisle. A flower girl in a white dress with a veil followed. The pianist began to play, 'Here comes the bride'. No one came. Everyone looked on in wonder. The pianist began again. Then, Lisa on her father's arm floated down the aisle.

The pastor gave a special wedding message that asked us to commit to them and their union. He talked about the importance of marriage. When he pronounced them husband and wife, they hugged and kissed. As they walked up the aisle, their faces radiated in smiles. Andy said something private to Lisa and she smacked him. He wore a microphone that hadn't been turned off. They laughed.

My relationship with my daughter blossomed. I received the gift of joy once again from my sweet pea. My spring baby had the perfect spring wedding.

ANOTHER APRIL BABY AND A MIRACLE MOVE

My mother always told me, "You're going to enjoy being a grandmother. There is nothing like it. Just wait and see." This proved to be true in the fall of 1996 when my first granddaughter joined us. My joy increased in the spring of 1998. I received the call in the middle of the night to come stay with my first grandchild. My second granddaughter arrived in the early morning on April 30th. The first year after her birth brought me incredible joy. My mother failed to warn me about the heartache that I could experience as a grandmother.

Lisa and Andy named my April granddaughter, Amanda Adelle. I had another sweet pea twenty-eight years later to love. She had lots of dark hair like her mother, older sister, and myself at birth. I had two precious girls seventeen months apart to see now. I visited almost every day even though I lived a good twenty minutes or so away.

I attended a wonderful church in Brighton and had started to work in a bank shortly after Amanda's birth. I floated between branches at my work. Many times I worked at locations near my daughter's home. I enjoyed the girls. Then, a year later, Andy got a new job in Grand Rapids.

The new job required a two hour move away from me. No more daily visits. I grieved the loss before the separation. I cried myself to sleep every night. People I worked with noticed my sadness. One of the ladies told me that a new branch would soon open in Grand Rapids. They didn't know if I could get a position there, but suggested I try. I hated to leave my church family, but I couldn't be separated from my girls, so I applied for the job and got the position.

In the spring of 1999, I traveled the highway to Grand Rapids to hunt for a place to live. My Ford Escort plowed through several inches of snow, typical bad weather for Michigan in March. I had a newspaper with apartment listings and a map. GPS didn't exist.

When I arrived in Grand Rapids, I called the first apartment listed. I had ten minutes to get to the rental office before it closed. Could I get there in time? I had never been to Grand Rapids before except for my job interview. The lady on the phone directed me to the apartment. The apartment complex had many hills and evergreen trees. I loved it and signed the lease right on the spot.

Lisa and Andy hadn't found a home yet. I could only hope their new home would be close to my new apartment. They found the perfect place less than a mile from my work.

My Brighton church family helped me locate a new place of worship. I hoped that it wouldn't be downtown. I felt intimidated by the size of Grand Rapids compared to Brighton. As it turned out, the church sat right next door to my apartment complex.

God blessed me with opened doors. He kept me together with my family and provided me with a new church family. I still hadn't married but my heart filled with thankfulness. Christ has redeemed me, transformed me over the years. He filled the empty space in my heart for a husband and became more than enough for me.

Isaiah 54:5 - For your Maker is your husband, The Lord of hosts is His name; And your Redeemer is the Holy One of Israel; He is called the God of the whole earth.

Shawn Gallagher

Shawn Gallagher is a retired special education teacher who now works as a visiting teacher and educational consultant for home-school and after-school students. Following the adages to "write what you know" and "write from the heart", her stories for this anthology are about students and families she's known and held close for years. Shawn's first published story appears in "Winter in the Mitten". She has been a member of the Shiawassee Area Writers for two years.

The Prankster

"You park like a moron." One glance at the bright orange ticket affixed to my windshield told me this wasn't a real citation, but it was a card full of angry comments. Its message was both startling and aggravating. I was accused of "dinging" a car when I knew I'd left plenty of space between vehicles at the Durand Union Station. More unsettling, the note was addressed to me personally, listing both my name and address.

"Great," I grumbled, "this lunatic knows where I live." But wait, how can that be? Was this someone I knew? Gazing around, I observed no one lingering about the near-empty lot. Muffled snickering from the back seat of the car answered my questions. The "Prankster" had struck again.

Joey had been a homeschooled student of mine for years. His mother, busy teaching an older sister, needed help. Joey was energetic and excitable; I was retired and willing. My journey with him began.

On this day, we were on an outing to the historic train station with his buddy, Jacob. Sauntering over to a vending machine, he asked to run back to the car for some quarters. "I know right where I left them. I'll be just a second." While Jacob and I strolled inside, his plan was hatched with careful precision. Joey was a seasoned prank-puller.

Over the years, I had been assaulted by squirting rings, snapping sticks of gum, rubber flies in my food and pillows toppling from opened doors. I had stepped in fake dog excrement, tried to wipe up imitation ketchup and been "beanboozled" by eating foul-tasting jelly beans snatched from the popular game and offered as an innocent treat. Shrieks of glee accompanied each victorious trick. Joey had a powerful affinity for mischief, and his sophistication and timing improved with each passing month.

His rap sheet began innocently enough: fake sneezes followed by handfuls of water tossed on his mother; plastic wrap under the cap of his sister's shampoo bottle; an occasional blast of "fart spray", delivered before an unsuspecting victim entered a room. Later, his stunts grew in boldness. One day I found myself reaching for toilet paper, only to be unable to rip it off the roll. Naturally, there were no spare rolls in sight—Joey had seen to that. My choices were to yell for help to the parents, mortified at how that rescue would play out, or gnaw the required sheets off with my teeth, which was what I was forced to do. The paper was stronger than cheesecloth and a definite clog threat in the older home. Joey told me later that this was one of his top three favorite pranks.

"I waited until I knew you had enough time, then I sneaked up to listen to you try to get help." Joey had no shame.

Determined not to be caught helpless again, I questioned him about his strategies. "I think about how you think," he confessed. I had been his teacher long enough for him to know me well.

My predictable squeamishness about unwiped noses prompted the "booger prank", number two on his hall of fame list. In this delightful caper, Joey innocently dropped a pencil, and stood up from retrieving it with a foot-long strand of nasal mucus hanging from his face. Trying to quell my rising gag reflex, I quickly looked away while pushing tissues in his direction.

"Here, here—use these."

Joey was delighted. "You and both of my grandmas did the exact same thing. They ran away with their faces all disgusted like yours." Joey believes his best victims are "you old ladies". According to him, we deliver the best reactions.

"What are you hoping for when you plan a prank?" I needed some clues in order to defend myself.

"I want you to scream or freak out and run."

This was precisely what happened one day last spring. When Joey's family moved from the suburbs to a farm surrounded by acres of woods, I was forced to confront some gruesome realities of nature. Family cats kill all kinds of small creatures—birds, chipmunks, baby bunnies—then deliver the kills to unsuspecting folks in pieces, a torso or leg here, a decapitated head there. Worse yet, the prey would be left alive and taunted through the final stages of the death struggle with playful pokes of the paw. My walk from the car to the door became quicker with each witnessed execution.

One day I was informed that over the weekend, one of the felines had appeared from near the front porch with a "huge" snake of unknown variety in its mouth. Since I had to pass that porch on my way in each day, I developed a substantial fear of confronting one of the giant reptiles, either in or out of a cat's mouth. My worst nightmare was realized one morning as one of the dreaded serpents slithered out from beneath a bush and glided across my path. As I screamed and jumped backward in fright, the snake suddenly began a retreat, sliding backward directly toward me. Frozen in place, I encountered Joey leaping happily from a nearby hiding place.

"I have you on video, too!" He could barely contain his excitement. There was, indeed, a security camera for recording outdoor intruders. My panic could now be viewed by all of Joey's appreciative pals. When I didn't laugh, he began to get nervous.

"Look, look. It's attached to a string. It's only a prank." School would be starting in a few minutes, and he was beginning to wonder if the consequences would backfire on him. Securing a promise that this would never happen again, I let it go.

Joey is always on the lookout for the next scare. He bargains with his dad to drive him to the local "Five Below", where his allowance money goes furthest. He stays well-informed as to their current stock of gags.

"What do you think about when you're shopping for a prank?" Maybe he'd slip and give me a tip. He'd taken a pause after the snake incident; the next fright would likely be soon.

"Well, I check to make sure it doesn't look fake or junky. I like to find ones that will gross everybody out, like the booger. I want to find one I can sneak in without anyone noticing, and I want ones we can laugh about later."

Lately Joey has incorporated his amazing talent for building elaborate chain-reaction structures into his hoaxes. An unsuspecting victim turns a door knob, only to spark a sequence of falling dominoes, collapsing wooden bridges, cars careening down ramps, and marbles whizzing through mazes. His creations are stunning and wonderfully clever.

"What do you hope will happen when you pull a prank?"

"I hope you and my parents will think I'm smart."

"We certainly do, Joey."

"Oh, and most of all, I want you to prank me back."

And, of course, I did--but that's another story.

Witness

On May 13, 1917, in a small rural village in Portugal, three young children tended to their family's sheep. The children were ten-year-old Lucia de Jesus dos Santos and her cousins, Francisco Marto, age nine and his sister Jacinta Marto, age seven. Around noon, the children prayed their rosaries, as was their custom in this predominantly Roman Catholic country. Afterward, while they played, a sudden flash of bright light alerted them to a possible approaching storm. They prepared to leave.

According to the children, a second flash of light illuminated a nearby holm oak tree, atop of which stood a lady "more brilliant than the sun." The little shepherds claimed that the woman told them she was from heaven and that she had a message for them to deliver, that prayer and repentance were needed to bring sinners back to God and an end to World War I. The children further reported that the lady asked them to return on the 13th of the next consecutive five months, at the same hour, for additional instruction.

The place was Cova da Iria, in the parish of Fatima, and the cousins did indeed return. Lucia, Francisco and Jacinta reported receiving messages and images, described as both wondrous and frightening, that convinced them they were communicating with Mary, the Mother of God. The woman in the vision asked the children to pray and make sacrifices for atonement of the world's evils and said she would be taking Francisco and Jacinta to heaven soon.

Lucia, she announced, would live a long life in service to God. The lady promised a "miracle" to demonstrate the authenticity of her identity and messages to the Portuguese people. She also asked that a chapel be built to mark her appearance.

The community, particularly the civil authorities, did not believe the children. Lucia's mother was horrified that her daughter would perpetuate such a lie. Though the Marto family supported Francisco and Jacinta, both families were worried how the quickly-spreading tale would affect their livelihoods. They tried to prevent their children from returning to the Cova. Despite being thrown into jail and threatened with death, the youngsters refused to deny their story. Eventually released, the cousins returned to the Cova on the appointed dates.

On October 13, 1917, exactly five months from the date of the first vision, the "Miracle of the Sun", as it came to be called, occurred in the Cova da Iria, Fatima. During the spectacle, a heavy downpour of rain was replaced by the appearance of the sun, changing form to resemble a silver disc. People reported seeing it "cartwheel upon itself" across the sky, spreading an array of colors on the ground before giving an impression of plunging toward earth. A crowd of 70,000 people were on hand to witness the phenomena, including many eyewitnesses who were non-believers and virulently anti-religious. At the end of the event, the ground and clothing of the people present became instantly dry. Reporters from local newspapers reported the story with photographs of the throngs of observers.

The story remained unchanged up to the death of Lucia in 2005. Lucia became a nun and claimed to have received further visits from "Our Lady of the Rosary," as she asked to be called. Francisco Marto and Jacinta Marto both died of the Spanish flu within three years of the apparitions. A major motion picture entitled "Miracle of Our Lady of Fatima" was released in 1952.

~

In the spring of 2018, I was invited by the Jafri family of Owosso, Michigan, to join them on a trip to Fatima. The parents, Ayaz and Laura, had been to Fatima in 1995 and were eager for their five children, ages 12 to 21, to share in their experience. Laura learned the story of Fatima from her devout grandmother, Jenny, who often took care of her and instructed her in the lessons of Catholicism. Laura's husband, Ayaz, is Muslim but participates in the Catholic faith. Their children are Catholic.

"We wanted to go to Fatima as a family. We didn't know if they would ever make it there as adults, and we wanted to make this journey together," Laura explained.

Not all Catholics are familiar with the story of Fatima, and of those who are, not all are believers. I had viewed the film with my mother as a young child and was excited to visit the site and learn the specific details of this unusual occurrence. My personal belief about the appearance was fluid. In preparation, I studied both its historical and religious background and was determined to remain open-minded. Once there, I would be watchful for evidence of truthfulness or exaggeration.

Our journey to Portugal had been formidable. Between missed plane connections and poor directions to our lodging, we arrived quite late at night. The logistics of managing the luggage of eight people up flights of stairs, finding an open restaurant and ordering in Portuguese had everyone's patience tried, however the Jafris have learned to remain calm in difficult times.

Two of their children have autism. Of the two, Sarah, now twenty years old, was more seriously affected than her brother, Jacob. It is very challenging for Sarah to express herself through speech; she is minimally verbal. Frustrated in communication, afflicted with seizures, and prone to episodes of anxiety, Sarah's parents feel she also has a unique connection to the divine.

"Sarah loves prayer. It makes her happy to pray. Although it's hard for her to sit still, focus and pay attention, this has never been the case in church." Her mother feels Sarah is drawn to representations of Joseph, Mary and Jesus. "She finds peace and comfort from looking at and collecting them. She likes to buy nativity sets and line them up around her for contemplation." Sarah often draws beautiful pictures of sacred images and carries them with her throughout the house. "Her life is not easy, yet she has an awareness of 'heavenly matters' .

~

Located within a large plaza, the "Chapel of the Apparitions" is a simple, pavilion-like structure having wooden benches on three sides facing a single, unadorned altar. Behind the altar is a statue of Mary, dressed in a long white gown, hands folded in prayer, holding a rosary. The statue marks the spot of the reported vision, the holm oak tree no longer standing. Various types of prayer services are held in the chapel each day. We elected to attend a mass in English at 2 p.m.

The service proceeded as usual. Scriptures were read, a homily was delivered, and a time of silent reflection followed. Suddenly, without a sound, Sarah rose to her feet with head bowed and hands clasped in reverence. She raised her eyes and fixed her gaze on the skylight directly above the statue of Mary. Standing absolutely motionless with what her mother accurately described as an "otherworldly" expression, this young lady with serious deficits in the ability to focus stood trance-like in prayer, hands clasped in reverence, for several moments. She kept her eyes on the skylight and never unfolded her "praying hands" as her family, the congregation, and I stared in surprise. Finally, Sarah slowly lowered herself back to her seat and the service continued.

I have known this young lady since she was three years old, and I was stunned at what I witnessed. The angelic pose and sweet expression of someone whose life had encompassed considerable struggle brought her mother and me to tears. Whatever she'd experienced remains her secret. As we left the chapel to tour the rest of the grounds, I asked, "Sarah, what did you see at mass?" Though she looked directly at me and gave no reply, I knew something had held her attention.

Afterward, Laura and I discussed what we had observed. "I can't explain it. I do believe that whomever or whatever is present to Sarah has its hands over her. It is listening to her, talking to her, connecting with her. Sarah is drawn intuitively to religious places and to visual images of her beliefs. That much I know. I also know that Sarah isn't worshipping idols. The statues of the Holy Family, the pictures and the crucifixes she wears evoke strong feelings of the peace her faith brings to her. What they remind her of is what matters to her."

~

Where do we draw strength for the treks through our personal trials? An infant clinging to life is soothed by sensation—a calming voice, the warmth of a blanket, a stroke on the hand. A child experiencing athletic defeat recalls the encouraging words of a trusted adult. As we age, we become aware of unexpected encounters with people or books we need to help us, just in time, through a troubling situation. Is it possible that for those who are unable to articulate need or draw conclusions from an "accidental" message, there is another path of spiritual reassurance? As for me, the journey to Fatima has convinced me that we can explore the miraculous by paying closer attention to the people in our everyday lives.

Sally Labadie

During forty years of owning and operating the Love Funeral Home with her husband, **Sally Labadie** saw how the village of Bancroft was losing its rich history with the death of the once active community leaders. This inspired her to compile *The History of Bancroft; A Pictorial History of the Town and Its People*, and to direct the Bancroft Historical Society.

Her own personal history of teaching and administration in the Corunna Public Schools was published in *The Good, the Oops! And the Funny, Events in the Life of a Teacher*, and was followed by *And You Thought I Retired*, memoirs of post retirement work in the Department of Education at Michigan State University. She continues to write memoirs of her life in rural Bancroft, Michigan, where she lives with her husband, Harold.

Teaching children has always been her mission, so she published six picture books and one chapter book; *Wooster the Rooster, Tanner's Turtle, The Schoolhouse Mouse, What's Under All Those Leaves, If I Had a Dinosaur, The Story of Honk, the Goose,* and *Mystery on the Cliffs.*

She is also a prolific writer of memoirs of her life in rural Bancroft and of adventures while fossil hunting with the Friends of the University of Michigan Museum of Paleontology. She also volunteers in classrooms at the Elsa Meyer Elementary School in Corunna, as well as at the Historical Village in Corunna.

Sally is a two year member of the Shiawassee Area Writers.

AH, SPRING!

May 1, 2006

Ah, Spring! The May apple is up, and I see sprigs that will be jack-in-the-pulpits, poking through last fall's leaf litter. The spring beauty is in full bloom, and the cut-leaf toothwort displays its pinkish white blossoms. Fern fronds are ready to uncurl, and the wild violets with their purple and yellow flowers dot the landscape. The woods are such an intriguing, colorful sight in the spring, and one must walk every day to see the changing colors and sprouting flowers.

There are times when I love the color and spring growth around my home. However, the color and growth sometimes brings unwelcome guests. I had watched the tulips poke through the ground in my flower bed, and within days, the tops were gnawed off by the rabbits or deer that inhabit the area around our home. I bought pepper-wax spray and doused what remained of the plants, thinking that would do the trick. But the rabbits and deer weren't the only animals that interrupted our enjoyment of spring.

This spring we were annoyed and somewhat fascinated by a particular body-slamming female cardinal. For three weeks, yes, three weeks, she kept slamming into two windows; one on the south side of our entrance hall, and the other on the west side of our living room. She banged and banged into a window and then sat in the bush under it and sang, but maybe it was scolding. Yes, female cardinals do have a voice. We put the cat in the window to no avail. We went to the window and shooed her off. We went outside and yelled. She always came back.

I checked the bushes for nests. I threw out an old dried-out one, and then within a couple of days, I found another one started on the same branch. My husband, Harold, said it was a robin's, but I tossed it anyway, just in case. The robin then built a nest in a nearby spruce tree. I put a sheet over the window, and taped up silhouettes of raptors. Nothing I did made a difference. She was there almost all day, slamming and scolding.

After three weeks the slamming became less frequent. She came only in the morning. Finally, there was peace! Hopefully she was nesting, and didn't have time to visit us. Either that, or her body gave out and she beat herself into oblivion. Now I could wash off the smeary marks she left on the windows.

With that interruption gone, another came along. I checked the tulips again, and I guess I didn't use enough spray or I needed to put a repeat application on, because the tulips were gone. Right down to the ground. The hungry critters also started in on my lilies and hollyhocks. I quickly sprayed everything with pepper spray and decided I'd check them daily.

We live in an area where there are acres of woods, farmers' fields and twenty acres permanently put into hay. But of course, my flowers are more appetizing.

Ah, Spring! What beauty! What next?

How Much of a Durango Would a Woodchuck Chew?

May 29, 2000

One of the exciting parts of being in the woods is that you never know what's there. You need to be alert to all movement, because the surprises can be memorable. On this particular Memorial Day, it proved to be just that.

I enjoy spending time with nature, keeping track of the flowers and signs of animal life. On this trip I decided to go to my favorite spot…our south woods, where the jack-in-the pulpit grows tall and the trillium, wild geranium and bedstraw grow thick. I drove the Durango this time, instead of taking the mile long walk…why, I don't know. I drove down the shaded lane and parked where a short, two-track trail made by my son, Ed's, tractor, leads to one of the corn fields.

As I walked across the grassy edge of the field, I paused when a small garter snake slithered almost under my feet. The tiny grasshoppers jumped as I disturbed the grass, their snapping noises filling the air. In the woods on the south side of the field is a swale, where Ed had dug a small pond for the deer. This had been a rainy spring, so the pond itself was invisible because water was covering the entire area of woods. I decided to forgo walking in that area.

I followed a small path through the trees to another field. As I approached the field, I heard a strange noise…like someone moving wood. It wasn't just a disturbance like deer might make in the brush, so I was concerned that someone was there. I stopped, crouched down, and peered through the trees, but saw nothing. I heard the noise again, so I cautiously retraced my steps for a short distance, and could hear the sound coming from inside a dead tree. Realizing it couldn't be a person, I stood and listened. I could hear scratching sounds from inside it. Could it be a raccoon? I tapped the tree and the noise stopped. It didn't seem to be something to worry about, so I decided to let it be.

I continued across the field to a rock pile in the edge of the woods, where I keep moving the rocks to make them more able to be washed with the rain. I picked up a small pudding stone. Pudding stones are unusual conglomerates, and since I love them, I show them off in my rock garden.

The mosquitoes were buzzing, and I was slapping them. They were pesky, but not enough to deter me. Blue flags, a kind of wild iris, were growing in a spot where I had never seen them before. A red-tailed hawk hovered above, giving his territorial cry, as he usually does when I am in the area.

I reached the Durango, opened the tailgate, and set the rock inside. I then backed the vehicle up, turning so I could head out easily. I sat there for a minute, but then decided my walk wasn't finished. There was another spot I wanted to check out. So, I walked to the meadow that stands on the western edge of the woods. The lane was shady, with the sunlight showing through in moving patches on the ground. Fresh scat was in the lane…about right for a fox. A rose-breasted grosbeak was trilling his song in a tall oak tree.

When I reached the meadow, I heard cardinals and finches

singing merrily. Yellow cinquefoil and hawkweed were prolific on the edge of the lane. After enjoying a peaceful few minutes, I returned to the Durango, trying to remember all I had seen so I could write this memoir.

I found a pad of paper and a pencil in the back seat pocket, sat in the driver's seat and started writing. I wasn't there more than a minute when I was distracted by a sudden movement on a small brush pile not twenty feet to the front and left of the Durango. A chipmunk was scampering over the pile of brush. I sat and watched the little critter. Suddenly, I saw something else moving near the chipmunk. On the edge of the brush pile was a woodchuck. He stopped and looked around, not seeming to notice me or the truck. I sat and watched, while writing down what was happening. He ambled to the other end of the brush pile where a small log was laying. He stretched out on it with his chin resting on the wood, and his legs dangling over the sides. He stayed there for several minutes. Oh, where was my camera? I hadn't brought it, and now I hated to leave! The chipmunk scampered around the woodchuck and disappeared.

The woodchuck, seemingly unfazed by the disappearance of the chipmunk, got up and walked toward me. He went to the front of my vehicle where I couldn't see him. I heard a scratching sound, (or was it chewing?) and then some soft thuds. What was he doing? Was he chewing the undercarriage of my truck? Nothing was visible from my window. There were just the soft thuds and the quiet sounds of him in the leaves and branches in the lane under my vehicle. After several minutes I said "enough!" and turned the key in the ignition. I didn't need to start the engine. The click alone frightened him. He scurried back to the brush pile, where he sat for a few more minutes, looking around to see where that sound came from, and probably wondering if he needed to escape quickly.

All was quiet, so he crossed the lane and slowly ambled through the woods, and toward the corn field, stopping only occasionally to look back.

I was pretty excited that I had come so close to such an animal, but I had been worried that he was chewing my truck! I drove to the woods at the farm where my husband and Ed were buzzing wood so I could share the excitement of what I had seen. Wrong choice! I also got to share in **their** fun by helping to buzz several loads of wood.

Mudbogging 101

April 10, 2001

I passed the beginning mudbogging class. As a woman at age 60, I did not intend to take the class, much less be introduced to the subject. One early spring day I drove to Marlette to help paleontologist Dr. Dan Fisher complete a search for mastodon bones. The air was crisp and the ground slightly frozen when I arrived at the site. The landowner was out at the road, and told me to drive on in. The work site was about a quarter mile in, with sticky clay, which I call muck, in the drive, and pools of icy water in the deep ruts from the large excavators. Since the ground was still a little frozen I got to the parking area after shifting into four wheel drive, and learning (fast) how to steer through the ruts.

We worked next to a cliff in a deep area of a future pond. There was an underground spring filling the hole, but a large sump pump was keeping most of the water out. Dan had already taken soil samples, cataloged and photographed the bone layer as well as the clay sub-bone layer.

The main reason for this weekend's quick work in snow was that it was the last weekend before the excavator would get back to work on the piles, which had been taken from near where some initial bone discoveries were made. Ribs, mandible and teeth, part of a pelvis, and numerous other smaller and broken bones had been retrieved from where the pond was being dug. The clay that had been removed was heaped into large piles, called spoils. The excavator would soon be used to level off the piles, and we needed to go through the piles to make sure all the bones were found.

We trudged up the drive to where there were more ruts and mucky clay. The clay stuck to my boots and the snow obscured my vision, but with shovels in hand, double gloves, knee boots and oh, yes…long johns to keep me warm, we made it to the piles. We shoveled the muck and heavy clay. We were looking for any bones that may have been moved by the excavator. It didn't look very promising!

At noon a student from Ann Arbor, five persons from Hale (including two teachers and two teenagers) and I were ready for a sandwich. At hunts like this I usually limit my liquid intake, as restroom facilities are often a little primitive. This time, the mud and snow were discouraging me from heading farther into the woods or behind the other piles, so water was off limits. We ate standing by a trailer filled with digging gear that the Hale residents had pulled. We had no place to sit. My hands grew numb and I became chilled from the lack of movement, so I headed back to the piles. The folks from Hale left, and Keith (another teacher) joined us.

The snow finally stopped but ice pelted our faces for some time. In mid-afternoon Keith left, and I decided to head out soon after. The temperature had risen just enough so that my boots had about five pounds of clay sticking to them. I trudged to the truck, with my shovels also weighing more from the sticky clay. I opened the rear door, put the shovel ends into a plastic bag and laid them in the back. I climbed into the back and Dan pulled my boots off and put them directly into another plastic bag. When I was fully in the rear of the Durango, he closed the tailgate. I crawled through the back and climbed over the seats in order to keep the mud out, checked to make sure I was still in four wheel drive, and hit the accelerator.

The mud flew and the truck slipped and slid, but it kept on moving. I steered around potholes of water, first to the right, then to the left, around the excavator...and precariously close to the cliff! The mud flew but I never slowed down. When I got out to the road, I honked to let Dan know I escaped safely, and drove around to the owner's driveway to thank them for letting us work there. I was in disbelief at the almost brown color of the bright blue Durango. Each wheel well was caked with mud and brown mud coated the entire vehicle. It was a first for me! **I passed Mudbogging 101!**

Carol Inman

Carol Inman is a writer of memoirs. She discovered her passion for writing while in high school. Each short story will take you on a journey to a moment in time to share her experience. Things she learned as a child growing up on a dairy and cash crop farm are shared in a teaching style. Her memoirs are historical accounts and written from personal knowledge. She will pull you into her life and captivate you into the story.

Growing up in rural Shiawassee County, she graduated from Corunna High School and received a Business Administration Degree from Baker College. She joined the Shiawassee Area Writers in 2018. She currently lives on a small farm near Bancroft with her husband, Wayne. They are the parents of three children, three grandchildren, and five great grandchildren.

What Friendship Looks Like

It is amazing what you learn in a fishing boat. I sat in a small boat on a private lake, listening to my dad's friend Ralph talk about the secrets to catching fish. It was my first time fishing with my dad and his friend. I remember Dad wore a straw hat and I wore a red babushka. The water was clear as glass on the sunny summer day as we drifted to a spot in the middle of the lake. Ralph said all the fish were here in this spot. Ralph put a red and white bobber on a line, a worm on the hook and handed me a pole. I cast the line in the water and waited.

Ralph liked to fish and invited my dad and me to go fishing with him. This lake was his favorite because of the large number of species of fish. His hope was to share his knowledge and encourage me to enjoy the sport. He showed us where schools of fish liked to feed. He began to tell us how he caught fish each and every time he visited this lake. He was patient. The boat rocked, and the warm sun on my face, and gentle breeze blowing through my hair made me feel relaxed. The quiet of nature filled my soul. Ralph had a teaching style that was simple and to the point.

Dad changed the subject. He and Ralph talked shop. They worked together at the Chevrolet factory on Chevrolet Avenue in Flint and enjoyed sharing their work experiences. Being only eight-years-old, I was excited about the day and while listening to their stories, forgot to watch my pole.

When the bobber disappeared and the tip of the pole splattered into the water, my dad said, "Whoa, fishing pole?" He reached over to steady the pole. This made me giggle. "Watch the bobber," he instructed, his finger pointing to the water. "When a fish comes nibbling, let him have a taste, then pull."

"Okay." I nodded.

As we waited, Dad watched the shoreline. He saw an animal and said, "Look on the shore at the rabbit in the shrubs. It's a cottontail. Wild carrots are one of their favorite foods." Dad enjoyed teaching me about the animals of the outdoors. I loved to listen to him and was eager to learn new things. Dad continued, "See the red squirrel jump from tree-to-tree. Squirrels are either fox, gray, or red. That one is a red squirrel. Squirrels prefer nut trees to gather and store nuts so they can stay active through the winter. Acorns from the oak trees were this squirrel's winter food. You can tell by all the acorn shells on the ground at the base of the white oak tree."

I asked my dad, "How do you know it's a white oak tree?"

Dad explained, "Oaks are broadly divided into two main groups; the red oak group and the white oak group. In general, trees in the red oak group have pointed lobed leaves and in the white oak group have rounded lobed leaves." I must have looked confused. My dad always carried a small pad and pencil in his shirt pocket.

He pulled it out and drew a sketch of the two different leaves to help me understand. He continued, "The leaves of the white oak are 4 to 9 inches long with 5 to 9 lobes. In summer leaves are bright green and turn red or brown in the fall. On young trees you may see leaves remain on the tree throughout winter. The acorn, fruit of the white oak, is a great food source for many animals and birds including raccoons, wild turkeys, squirrels, chipmunks, and crows."

"Oh, that one is the white oak," I exclaimed as I pointed to one of my dad's drawings. I could tell by the smile on my Dad's face that I had guessed correctly. It felt good to know that I had the correct answer.

I began thinking out loud. "Do squirrels know the difference between red and white?"

Dad seemed to realize that I needed more information, and he was ready. "Acorn development is different between these two groups. Acorns in the white oak group are sweet and mature in one season. It takes two years for acorns in the red oak group to mature. Red oak acorns are very bitter tasting. So, squirrels and other wild animals, prefer acorns from the white oak and work all season to store them for winter food.

"Are you here to fish or talk all day about nature and the things of the outdoors?" Ralph inquired. "Would you like to know about fish? It is my turn to talk and your turn to listen." Ralph sounded irritated and must have felt left out of my Dad's animal and tree explanation.

I sat up and responded with what I believed to be a fishy question, "Are salmon in this lake?" I knew the answer. Ralph knew that I knew the answer to my question.

Ralph responded, "No, salmon are, for the most part, found in the big waters. They are not usually found in small lakes like this one. Here you can catch bluegills, crappies, sunfish, yellow perch, and maybe walleye."

I felt a fish nibble my worm. The bobber went down in the water out of site. "Pull," Ralph yelled, "You caught a bluegill. It is a keeper! Bluegills are freshwater sunfish." Ralph was teaching more about fish. He continued, "You are not fishing. You are catching!" He was excited for me. Soon we began to catch fish, one after another until we had enough for a meal and extra for the freezer.

It was time to pull the lines and head for the boat launch. We had fish to clean. Cleaning the fish made a smell that made me cough, gag, and sneeze. Ralph teased, "Oh, does it smell?"

I snapped. "It smells terrible. It stinks!"

It was time to go home. Dad thanked Ralph. "This is a great place to fish, easy to access, has a high likelihood of catching fish, and is all-around family friendly! Thank you for inviting us." I was happy that Ralph liked to fish and took this day to share his knowledge and experience with us. He taught us secrets to catch fish. He showed us where schools of fish liked to feed, and what species are in this lake. He used a bobber, worm, small pole, and patience. He used simple teaching instructions for my young mind. I wanted to come again. I was sure that I would remember this day.

It was my turn to teach Ralph. I stated, "My mom taught me that the Bible is not a novel and not a magazine." I continued, "You find God in all things. When God creates something, rabbits, squirrels, oak trees, bluegills and friends, oo la la!" I giggled. I liked to memorize Bible verses. I recited this memory verse for my dad and Ralph. "All wild animals and birds and fish will be afraid of you," God told Noah, "for I have placed them in your power, and they are yours to use for food, in addition to grain and vegetables. Genesis 9:2"

Spending time with my dad and his friend that day was a true gift from God as Dad was always busy with work and the farm. Ralph and my Dad had taught me many things that day, and I liked sharing what I knew about nature with them.

Cyndy Habermehl

Cyndy Habermehl is a graduate of Baker College, Owosso, with an Associates of Applied Science Degree. After thirty years working in the medical field, Cyndy is now enjoying her retirement years by writing memoirs, poetry and children's books. Her previous publications include writings in *Winter in the Mitten*, published in 2018 by Shiawassee Area Writers.

She lives with her husband, Lee, and they both live near the farm she grew up on, also where these stories originated.

Sheep Shearing Time at Grandfather's Farm

The season of spring is a welcome time on the farm. There is so much activity going on, especially as the days get longer and the breezes chase away the damp air of winter. As a girl, I can recall going to school during the week, but when the weekend came, I was able to be part of the farm activities. One particular Saturday each spring was spent focusing on shearing the sheep. My grandfather lived on the next farm down the road, just down the hill from the farm I lived on. He owned a flock of sheep, maybe 30 or so.

On that day, I walked down the road to my grandparents' house. I waited inside until the sheep shearing men arrived in their pickup truck. They brought large equipment and unloaded it onto the barn floor. They were always loud in their talking and laughter. When they were all set up, Grandpa opened the large back door to the barn and called to the sheep. Sheep will come to their owner when called. This usually brought them from far out in the pasture. The sheep were herded onto the barn floor, making loud bleating sounds as they were probably nervous about what was to come next. Grandpa had them in a fenced in area near where the shearers had set up.

He would catch one of the large ewes by a leg and move her onto the shearer's wooden platform. At that time, the sheep would be set up on her bottom and the shearing of the wool from the sheep began. The clackity clack of the shearing and the bleating of the sheep made a strange duet. Sometimes, the shearers chewed tobacco and spit on the heads of the electric shears. I did not like this part and I turned my head away so I didn't see it.

Upon finishing that sheep, the animal stood up and went off to another area. After being shorn, the animal looked somewhat cold and bare. Grandpa then picked up the wool from the floor and carried it over to an area where he had a table. The table had a special set up where the twine was strung between notches. He lay the wool in the middle and brought up the hinged sides of the box. He tied off the twine in seaman's knots. He released the table to lie flat again. He then threw the bale of wool upstairs to a clean area in the haymow. I stacked the bales into a neat pile.

The process would continue throughout the rest of the morning and into early afternoon, until every sheep was shorn. It was then that I was asked to leave the barn and the doors were closed. The men then changed out of their oily and greasy overalls into street clothes.

I went into my grandmother's house and she would offer me cookies and milk. I especially liked the molasses cookies. She bought them at Conklin's bakery in Durand. The cookie was big. It had a jelly center cut out, which I saved eating until the last.

The next day, Sunday, a truck arrived to pick up the bales of wool. It backed up the length of grandfather's driveway and the bales were loaded. I understood they were to be taken to a location where they were cleaned up and knit into sweaters and coats for people.

At times in my life, people have asked me if I like to eat lamb. I have to say that it does not interest me too much after growing up on a farm and working with the sheep. I do like the memories it has afforded me and I love to see little lambs in the spring, at play in the fields.

Spring Cleaning

Daylight comes early,
Revealing cobwebs and dust
Once hidden by shorter, darker days.
Now, motivation is prompted and a must!

Line up the buckets, rags and cleaners,
Turn on the stereo music loud.
All hands on deck as we begin
To clean our house and make Mama proud!

Elizabeth Wehman

Elizabeth Wehman's writing career spans over thirty years beginning with publications in various Christian periodicals. From there, she was a newspaper reporter for six years at *The Owosso Argus Press* and then eight years for the *Owosso Independent.*

In 2014, Elizabeth published her first fiction, *Under the Windowsill,* followed by *Promise at Daybreak, Just a Train Ride* and her latest work, *Mere Reflection,* in May 2019. She continues to pursue a career in fiction writing with plans on a mid-Michigan farming wives series later in 2019.

Elizabeth formed the group, Shiawassee Area Writers, in spring of 2017. The group's membership is now 35 members who meet twice a month to discuss writing and offer a place to network with others doing the same.

You can follow Elizabeth on FB at: Elizabeth Wehman/Author, on Twitter at: @ElizabethWehman and on her website at www.elizabethwehman.com. She is also profiled in Good Reads and Bublish. Her books are also available on her website as well as Amazon.com.

Sometimes...Lessons Hurt

I'd wanted one my whole life. It was listed on every Christmas or birthday list. I could only imagine the joy that would come from owning a four-legged friend. Yet celebrations went by and my dream of having a dog disappeared with every unwrapped box.

It wasn't my parents' fault. They had legitimate reasons why I couldn't have one; we *lived in an apartment, our backyard wasn't big enough, Grandma's allergic.* They'd even added, *I wasn't old enough for such a responsibility.* I knew better.

Taking care of a pet, especially a dog, could never be a chore. I'd have a forever friend. We'd have a family watchdog. He'd sleep with me during winter nights and tag behind me on fishing days.

As my fourteenth birthday approached, I put a new puppy on my wish list. Mom gave me the *look.* "Caleb? There's *only* one thing on your list."

I gave her the infamous smirk that always made her pinch my cheek.

Tossing the list back she said, "You know. You have to come up with something else, right?"

I shrugged. "A puppy is all I want."

The family gathered on my birthday. My Mom made my favorite meal. Spaghetti. As the whiff of garlic bread spread through the kitchen, I looked around the room for presents. Hope increased until I noticed several wrapped packages on the table. My heart sank.

"Where's Dad?"

"He's coming. He had a long day," Mom said as she placed a garlic bread basket on the table.

My Dad had been putting in extra hours at work. It wasn't unusual for him to miss dinner. But today was my birthday. Surely, he would be here.

As I contemplated this, my grandparents came through the back door with smiles and greetings. My younger brother and sisters scrambled to greet them. As Gramps made his way to me, he ruffled my hair. "Hey birthday boy!"

"Hey Gramps."

Rubbing his hands together, he smiled at my Mom. "Sarah, it smells delicious."

My Grandmother came up from behind me and kissed my head. "Happy Birthday Caleb."

"Thanks Grandma."

I put elbows on the table, my chin resting on the heels of my hands and sighed as another wrapped box was placed beside my plate.

Soon the table was loaded with my favorite foods. Mom pulled back a curtain at the window. "Your Dad is really running late. I'm not sure if we should wait or not."

All the kids plopped down into their chairs. Waiting to eat would be a laborious task for them. Even Gramps sat down in Dad's chair adding, "Honey, I'm starving. Grant can catch up when he gets home."

Mom nodded. "Yes, let's go ahead."

Gramps had everyone hold hands. "Let's thank God for our food."

I took the hand of my little brother and also the soft, warm hand of my Mom. She always tried hard to make our birthdays special. Whatever happened, I'd do my best to be grateful.

As Gramps finished praying, Dad burst through the door. When I focused on him, large brown eyes caught mine. A bark announced, "I'm here!"

My chair fell backward as I jumped and headed for the warm, squiggly puppy in Dad's arms. Dad grinned as he held out the dog to me. "Happy Birthday Caleb."

The puppy crawled up my chest and a warm, rough little tongue kissed my eyelids and cheeks. He was perfect. My younger siblings wanted nothing more than to hold and pet him, but I struggled to share. I'd spent my whole life waiting for this moment and I wanted this puppy to bond with me.

To my surprise and relief, the wrapped presents included a dog's collar, puppy toys, and a leash.

I named my puppy, Duke. Duke was a brown, fluffy, needy ball of fur. He had a hard time remembering what to do outdoors. We went through paper towels like crazy. Every night, I was out on the back porch waiting for Duke. As frustrating as it was, so late at night, it was nice to hear the frogs croak in the pond down the road. Spring was in the air.

Dad let Duke sleep with me. I'd often stir awake to his puppy licks on my face. He only needed a little sleep and then wanted nothing more than to play. I grew so tired that first week. I'd come home from school needing a nap, but Duke wanted to take a walk or play.

My Mom laughed at my sleepy antics. One afternoon, I put the milk from my afternoon snack into the pantry instead of the refrigerator. "You're like a new Daddy, Caleb, with a new baby in the house." I didn't quite understand what she meant, but laughed anyway.

Easter services were coming. My siblings had set out their empty Easter baskets and were excited to have them filled with candy and special surprises. Duke wanted to play with the colored grass in each one. My sister got mad at him every time she found her basket empty and purple grass spread around the living room.

Good Friday came and we were preparing to head to the services at church that afternoon. The puppy had kept me awake almost every hour the night before.

With no school that day, my siblings were playing outside all morning. Mom kept issuing scolding reminders to shut the back door, but bugs still infiltrated her kitchen.

As I sat on the couch just before church, I laid my head down on a pillow while watching Duke play with a new band of twisted rope I'd gotten him as a present for Easter. Holding it between his paws, he chewed at the cords.

I startled awake when Mom shook my shoulder. "Caleb."

Sitting up, rubbing my eyes, I answered. "Oh man. I must have fallen asleep."

My Mom's eyes were red as if she'd been crying. She sat down and put her arm around me.

"Caleb. Duke got outside."

I glanced around the room in a panic. "What? Where is he?"

Lowering her head, tears now spilled off her cheeks, dampening the front of her shirt.

"Mom, what's wrong?"

At that moment, Dad came into the room, his face grim. "Caleb, I'm sorry buddy. Someone must have left the kitchen door open."

Why was Mom crying? What was Dad saying? I couldn't decipher what was happening through the fog of my nap.

I glanced around the room. "Where's Duke?" As much as I wanted to know, I was afraid to hear the answer.

We buried my puppy behind the shed. My brother and sisters wore their church clothes for that afternoon's Good Friday service.

They all tried to say something nice about Duke. I knew each one felt guilty for leaving the door open. Even though they'd all confessed, knowing the culprit wouldn't bring Duke back.

My Mom hugged me. "I'm so sorry, Caleb. I should have been watching him better."

Duke had ventured across the busy road in front of the house. The man who hit him admitted, "He's so little. I didn't see him until it was too late."

My dream. The one thing I'd wanted my entire life was gone. He was now buried beneath the cold ground. Never to be a part of my life again.

Going to my bedroom, I cried harder than a fourteen-year-old would want anyone to know.

We were supposed to head to church that afternoon. I had refused to get ready, but Dad convinced me that sometimes the best thing to do was go to church. Today was an important day to remember. He didn't want the whole family to go without me. I tried to explain, through my tears, that I didn't think I could stop crying long enough and how embarrassed I'd be, but he told me it was time to be a man.

I didn't understand the reason why he was insistent that I go, especially after what had happened. I glanced over at the puppy bed still occupying the corner of my bedroom. My tears continued as I got up and dressed for church.

Everyone was silent on the way. I couldn't look at anyone. My anger overpowered my ability to talk. I knew no one had left the door open on purpose nor had they wanted Duke to get hit on the road, but I had to be angry at someone. It would take a long time before I could forgive them. I knew that. My heart grew hard as bitterness filled my soul.

My church is a friendly place. Everyone asks how you are, shakes your hand, despite your age. How would I ever get through that without tears? My Dad seemed to understand. He said, "Caleb, stay here." Leaning over to my Mom, he gripped her hand. "Save us a seat." She and my siblings left the car.

Dad drove around the parking lot several times, even passing open spots. We were running late. This would make us even later. Finally, selecting a spot he'd passed probably three times, he turned off the car and just sat there without getting out.

"Caleb, I know this is a horrible day for you. I feel so bad that you lost Duke. Let's take a moment before we head into the building."

He seemed to sense how I was feeling. Going in late would prevent me from having to talk to people. Sure enough, he seemed to protect me as we scooted into the pew beside Mom. She took my arm as the service began.

It seemed like a normal church service, but a bit subdued due to the reason we were all there. Good Friday is a celebration of sorts for those who see Jesus as a Savior. The service is to remember the day when an innocent person was put on trial and to death for no other reason than claiming to be God.

Death wasn't something I wanted to remember or celebrate on this day. I had to say goodbye to something I'd looked forward to for so long. It was hard to believe that Duke had been with me just a short time and now he was gone.

The pastor told the story of John. John was one of Jesus's closest friends. Jesus had even asked John to take care of his mother while He was dying on the cross. John had probably loved Jesus and had given up his life to follow Him. He expected Jesus to be with him forever. His miracles and way of living had given John hope and security. And now, Jesus was gone. Dead.

Then the Pastor talked about Mary, Jesus' mother. She was watching her Son die on a cross. I glanced at my mother. She was still clutching my arm. She knew how much I hurt today and was right there with me sharing my sadness more than I probably even knew.

How sad this day was for everyone who knew and loved Jesus. They felt the same loss as I felt. Someone they longed to have with them, who had brought them hope and happiness, had just been crucified. In their hearts, for all they knew, he was gone forever. They didn't know about Easter morning yet.

Leaving church that afternoon, I realized how much I would miss my puppy. The sermon helped me relate to those who loved Jesus and how much they lost on that day so long ago. Jesus wasn't a puppy, but someone very special. How sad they must have been on that horrible day. It put my situation into a different perspective. I loved my dog, but I'm sure God the Father, watching His Son die on a cross, felt even greater pain.

When we all got into the car, Dad turned to me. "Son, do you realize now how much God loved us to sacrifice His Son for us? Did you feel the sorrow others might have felt when Jesus was put to death for no reason? Do you understand that better now?"

I nodded. "A little, but Duke was just a puppy, not the Son of God."

My Dad smiled, "But know that the best part of that story was, He didn't stay dead. We know that because we know the whole story. Sadness is but a time, but Jesus soon arose from the dead. He didn't stay dead."

With that, my Dad turned around and headed in the opposite direction from our house.

My little brother was the first to ask, "Where are we going, Dad?"

"You'll see."

The van pulled into a strange driveway. We all sat in our seats as he got out of the car and went to the front door of the house.

"What's Dad doing, Mom?" I unbuckled my seat belt and scooted myself between the space of the front seats, over the car's console.

"You'll see."

Dad returned to the car. He opened the door and said, "Son, today was a hard day for you. I'm proud of how well you obeyed me to go to church and hear about death and sadness even though your heart hurt, but I think you understand better than ever today the importance of why Jesus did what He did for us."

I nodded.

"This is Duke's first home. Out back there are three more puppies. Duke's brothers. I think Duke would want you to love one of them, just like you did him."

I couldn't believe it.

"Only if you want. If you'd rather not, I understand. None of them are Duke, but I'm sure all of them would like to be loved like Duke."

I wasn't sure what I wanted at that moment but said, "Can we go see them?"

Dad put his arm around my shoulders, "Yup. Let's go."

Entering the backyard, we found three puppies exactly like Duke stumbling over each other to greet us.

"Don't ever forget your lesson today, son. When Jesus died for us, it was a horrible day. But what John and his mother Mary didn't know was...Easter was coming!"

I picked up one of the excited puppies who did just what Duke had done to me a few days before. As the little guy licked my face, I felt a bit of hope fill my heart. It wasn't Duke and I'd have to start all over again training this puppy like I had done with him, but he might bring me joy just like Duke had done.

"I'd like to take him home, Dad."

Dad paid the owner for my new puppy and we headed back to the car.

That happened so many years ago. It helped me understand better the suffering others felt because of Jesus' death and to realize that sometimes we don't know the whole story, but God always knows what is best. Throughout his life, my father taught me many lessons. To help me remember this particular lesson, I decided to name my new puppy John. He brought me joy for the next fifteen years.

Brenda Stroub

Brenda Stroub is a born again Christian who wants to share Christ's love to others. She has always enjoyed writing testimonials, personal essays, memoirs, prose, and journaling. Being a part of the Shiawassee Area Writers group has been a rewarding and educational experience for her. A great release of giving back, a portion of what she has been given; a process full of blessings.

She has been a member of Shiawassee Area Writers for two years and published in their first anthology, *Winter in The Mitten*.

Brenda has previously been employed as a secretary, office manager, payment solutions coordinator, and a Certified Dental Practice Management Administrator. Another way she loves to communicate to the world is through sign language. She was a deaf interpreter at church for three years, and has taught sign language as well.

Brenda was born in Flint, and graduated from Durand High School. She has also lived in Dayton, and now resides in Lennon with her husband, Kip. They have two adult children and ten grandchildren. You can find more about her on Facebook.

The First Day

She awoke in a fog, on a gentle spring morning, almost not remembering for a brief moment that her life would never be the same. All she had left to cling to were memories.

Yesterday was the day she had been dreading for years. Losing her husband after 50 years of marriage was going to be her hardest battle to overcome. At least she had God's promise he was now in Heaven and she would join him again someday. But that left a long, lonely day ahead filled with endless reminders of their life together.

She no longer remembered how to function without him. He had filled her days with laughter and love, always making her feel safe and taking care of her every need. She would have to find a way by herself now.

God promised to direct her path. She would seek His help throughout the day, to fill all the empty, aching spots that arose and see where He would take her. She prayed for His leadership to fill her with purpose and direction, knowing that everything would be okay as long as she kept her focus on Him. He had always been there. She knew His plan was perfect and would be the very best for her.

She took a deep breath, sat up, put her feet on the floor and got out of bed. It was the dawn of a new beginning, the birth of a widow. She took the first step, holding her head high. She felt the spring sunshine caressing her face through the window, a reminder that she was not alone.

Spring Surroundings

God, you are the crisp March air I breathe.
You are the sun shining down on me.
You are the spring breeze caressing my face.
You are the grass beneath my feet.

God, you surround me with your presence.
You are the waves of the oceans.
You are the strength of the mountains.
You are the gravity of the universe.
God, you surround me with your power.

You are the gentle April rain falling on my head.
You are the warm sand that covers the beach.
You are the clouds above me.
God, you surround me with your peace.

You are the May rainbow hanging in the sky.
You are the stars that glisten at night.
You are the sounds of nature.
God, you surround me with your love.

You are the fragrance of the flowers in June.
You are the beauty I see in everything.
You are the Christ in me.
God, you surround me.

Easter Thoughts
An Acronym

E - Everlasting love

Are you a minister of God and His everlasting love? Let your life testify to it. We are not perfect but are a   work in progress. How is your journey going? You don't have to travel alone; all things are possible with God.

2 Corinthians 6:4-10 - "But in all things approving ourselves as the ministers of God…"

2 Corinthians 5:20 – "Now then we are ambassadors for Christ…"

A - Amazing grace

We can have Easter every day; choose not to dwell and die in the negative, but to arise and live in the positive. Dance to the music of His life in you; live the joy. We are the reason He came. We are no longer hopeless or helpless. In Him, we have everything we need. He has not left us empty-handed. Celebrate His amazing grace.

John 10:10 – "The thief cometh not, but for to steal, and to kill, and to destroy: I am come that they might have life, and that they might have [it] more abundantly."

S - Sacrifice

Jesus Christ died because of me, now I live because of Him. It wasn't a partial death; He gave it all. There is no need to be a part-time Christian. Don't go halfway. Don't hold back. Jump all the way in.

Matthew 18:11 – "For the Son of man is come to save that which was lost."

John 3:16 – "For God so loved the world that he gave his only begotten

Son, that whosoever believeth in him should not perish, but have everlasting life."

T - Totally complete

On Good Friday, Jesus said, *"It is finished." John 19:30.*

I am overcome with this day and what it means in history. Today and forever all through eternity; everything was accomplished in the power of a moment.

E - Eternity

Death is the doorway to eternity. Do you know where you will spend it? Make sure you know your destination. There is a big difference between I think so and I know so.

1 John 5:13 – "These things have I written unto you that believe on the name of the Son of God; that ye may know that ye have eternal life, and that ye may believe on the name of the Son of God."

Eternal life is not determined by our good works, but by our personal belief in who Jesus is, the Son of God.

Eph 8 & 9 – "For by grace are ye saved through faith; and not of yourselves: it is the gift of God: not of works, lest any man should boast."

R - Redeemed

Remember the sacrifice, for without the cross and the blood there would be no redemption, no forgiveness, no salvation, and no victory.

Heavenly Father, make me a compass that always points people toward Christ.

Praise the Lord for His unspeakable gift. The unsearchable riches of Christ.

On March 24th, 1975, I placed my life into the hands of God and accepted Jesus as my Lord and Savior. I had nothing to lose and everything to gain. My life has never been the same, because now I am touched by the Master's Hands. Jesus has made all the difference. He saved me from hell, forgave me of my sin, and now I am born again; this time, born of the spirit not the flesh and this time, because I choose it. Christ lives in me, the hope of Glory. Please don't wait. Time is getting shorter every day.

Col 1:27 – "To whom God would make known what is the riches of the glory of this mystery among the Gentiles; which is Christ in you, the hope of glory."

-Scriptures used are taken from the King James Version (KJV), public domain.

Our Amazing Spring Adventure

I could hardly contain my anticipation. The days weren't going by fast enough. For our 45th wedding anniversary, my husband promised to kiss me at the Grand Canyon; my first trip out west. We planned to leave after I retired in April. I found it hard to get through my final days at work. We had purchased a motorhome the year before and had a trailer built to accommodate hauling our car.

We scheduled reservations at campgrounds around our major destinations and would be staying in Walmart parking lots along the way. The planned highlights were: Mt. Rushmore, Yellowstone National Park, the Grand Canyon, and the Passion Play in Arkansas.

I couldn't imagine going to these far away places or being married for 45 years. It was also a momentous occasion because we would be celebrating my husband being cancer-free for two years. God had given us more time together to make some wonderful memories commemorating these special blessings.

After leaving Mason, our husky-lab mix, in the neighbor's care, we started our journey from Michigan. Our first spot would be Custer, South Dakota. I had a special travel journal to keep track of our mileage, expenses, and thoughts along the way. And of course, my camera, to capture every breath-taking view. Kip is a retired truck driver with over three million miles under his belt. I definitely felt safe and secure with him behind the wheel. After a prayer of gratitude and asking for God's protection, we pulled out of town.

Unexpectedly, we spent our first night just outside of Chicago at an RV repair shop. Thank God, our motorhome only required a minor fix and the repair shop was able to take care of us right away.

I was amazed at how the landscape changed from one state to another. We traveled through Iowa and Minnesota with the first leg of our journey complete.

Crossing into mountain time, we saw prairies, white cows and huge haystacks as big as cars. First we saw the Badlands; which were unbelievable. Arriving in Custer, South Dakota, we spent the next day at Crazy Horse and Mt. Rushmore. It felt like we could reach out and touch the presidents' faces; what an awesome sight.

Next we took Needles Highway, a one lane road and saw more amazing views. Only cars are allowed through the tunnels in the rock-faced mountain structures. Traveling through Custer State Park in the Lower Wildlife Refuge, we spotted our first bison.

On our way back to camp, we saw a church sign and thought we'd stop to check it out. As we pulled into the parking lot, a couple came walking out. It looked like they'd been cleaning the church. To our surprise, it was the Pastor and his wife. He told us it would be fine to park our motorhome and trailer right out front on Sunday morning. We will never forget the Mountainview Baptist Church. It reminded my husband of his childhood church, Oak Street Baptist. It seemed like stepping back in time, with the boys dressed in white shirts and ties, shoes shined and their hair cut short. A respectful, sincere and gracious group of believers. They still continue to inspire us.

As we traveled through Wyoming and Montana, I marveled at

the great vastness of the plains and the large mountain ranges. They seemed to go on forever. I wondered how anyone could possibly see all the amazing landscape without seeing God as the Creator. We saw sagebrush and noticed how different the pine trees were. Even the air felt more dry.

The white-capped Grand Teton Mountains were breathtaking. They were so large that the other mountains looked black in their shadow. When we headed downhill from a mountain, Kip would say, "whee!", and I'd only lift my head long enough to take a quick picture.

We passed a triple tandem semi-trailer for the first time, as we pulled into Yellowstone National Park. In Idaho, the winds whipped at us through the valleys and we saw five elk at a local park.

Mammoth Hot Springs and Old Faithful were also amazing sights. We could actually smell the sulfur in the air, and the trees were burnt white at the bottom of the Geyser Basin. There was a multitude of wildlife including elk and buffalo dotting the horizon. We passed a buffalo lying down on the shoulder of the road. The Yellowstone River looked bright blue with wild daisies along the shoreline. Leaving Yellowstone, as we crossed the Continental Divide. A large field of mustard was growing on the other side.

Entering Utah, we saw dust funnels that looked like mini tornadoes spinning around on the desert floor. In Salt Lake City, the ground was white with salt. From there, we traveled through Ogden and Orem. The expressway was eight lanes wide on each side packed with cars. The hillsides were covered with dead trees from heat fires. Our ears popped from changing altitude to 6600 feet. The mountains weren't as overbearing as in the beginning.

At 113 degrees, we entered Nevada and everything became hot to the touch. The mountains turned to a beautiful red and coral orange color. The roads became curvy going into Arizona. Upon entering the Virgin Mountains, we saw large cacti. We passed desert sands and yucca plants. Palm trees peppered the roadsides. We even saw a dead coyote. There were fields of solar panels and large power plants. In the desert, we saw trees growing right out of the sand. The headwinds were so strong at one point they picked up our motorhome and trailer setting us down in the other lane…eek! Thank God there were no cars; the episode took our breath away.

The scenery changed drastically in Arizona with no foliage and a completely dry, dirt landscape. We traveled Route 66 into Williams, Arizona. In the thick air, I found it hard to breathe and had to chug a bottle of ice-cold water to bring my temperature down. We stayed there for three days to take a break and see the Grand Canyon on our anniversary. We had ice cream, relaxed in the hot tub and took cold showers before visiting Bearizona Wildlife Park.

After breakfast the next day, we boarded the Grand Canyon Railway. A nice lady in our train car asked Kip our secret to making our marriage last. Kip said, "It can't be done without the Lord Jesus Christ. It took me a long time to figure it out." Next we experienced the awesome canyon with a spectacular kiss on the lookout point at 7000 feet altitude. I'll never forget it. We had a wonderful dinner at the Railway Buffet while a musician played a guitar.

We left Arizona a couple of weeks before the monsoon season. Heading through New Mexico, we saw Ponderosa Pines and large cattails. I felt like Moses, as if I'd walked on holy ground and I'd never be quite the same with all I'd seen and experienced on our trip. Each morning I would wake up and say, "Honey, what amazing sights are you going to show me today?"

Outside of New Mexico, we passed the Dead River. It was a wide, dry riverbed. Viewing mountains every day with open land and gusty winds that pummeled us between the pink-topped cactus bushes and coral desert sands. We saw a white-tailed lizard, New Mexico's state animal.

Heading into Texas, we passed more green pastures and turbine farms as far as the eye could see. For the first time in weeks, we saw no mountains in the distance, just flat lands for miles. Pastures were full of large cows and Texas Longhorns.

Then came Oklahoma and into the Ozarks of Arkansas. We had an amazing time watching the Passion Play in Eureka Springs. The actors made the stories of the Bible come alive. While touring the displays, we made friends with a nice couple that we still keep in touch with occasionally. The gentleman, Rick, said he loved meeting people he would be spending eternity with in Heaven.

Our final destination was in Shawnee, Kansas, where we shared dinner with Kip's brother and family. We had a great visit and soon headed for home.

Even though we had an amazing adventure, out of all the wonderful places we had been, Shiawassee County, Michigan, is still the only place for us. We traveled 5,220 miles in 21 days and were so happy to be back home, near family and friends again. These awesome memories still bring tears to my eyes. I'm so thankful we were able to experience them together.

Nancy Thompson Walther

Nancy Thompson Walther likes to think creatively, trying new and different styles with her art and writing. Her works of poetry are free verse. She has included introductory paragraphs that share her inspiration for each poem. She created them with thoughtfulness, prayer, and faith.

Nancy was born in Detroit and grew up in Livonia. After she married, she moved to Dearborn and then to Argentine Township. She enjoys being a wife and a mother. She is a part-time caregiver to her son, who deals with many medical challenges.

Nancy and her husband met on a blind date. They married a year later, on October 28, 1995. They love going on train tours and looking at the fall colors for their anniversary.

Her son is Byron Area Schools graduate. He attends Washtenaw Community College and works at IHOP. Silver, their 16-year-old cat likes eating, napping in his cardboard box, and playing with bubbles.

Nancy's hobbies include thrift store shopping, crafting and upcycling, gardening, going on walks, and playing Words with Friends. Her blog can be found at https://won-pet-status.com that showcases her various hobbies.

A collection of poems inspired by
A Red Morning Sky

Vivid red, orange, yellow, and smoldering gray hues wove across the sky one morning. The magnificent scenery captivated me. My soul also felt uneasy, because it looked like everything was on fire. A red sky in the morning is a symbol bad weather, or difficult times, are ahead. It inspired me to write poetry celebrating the beauty of coping with loss and tribulation.

"1 Therefore being justified by faith, we have peace with God through our Lord Jesus Christ:2 By whom also we have access by faith into this grace wherein we stand, and rejoice in hope of the glory of God.3 And not only so, but we glory in tribulations also: knowing that tribulation worketh patience;4 And patience, experience; and experience, hope:5 And hope maketh not ashamed; because the love of God is shed abroad in our hearts by the Holy Ghost which is given unto us.6 For when we were yet without strength, in due time Christ died for the ungodly." (Romans 5:1-6 King James Version)

My first poem, Justified, is an Anaphora poem. The words "I am" typed first in every line create its rhythm. It expresses the power of Jesus's death on the cross. Believing in Jesus's gift of love gives me the freedom to have hope during hardship.

Justified

I am
I am the holy of holies
I am the spring joy
I am the red morning sky
I am the fiery ruby of atonement
I am the regal orange of strength
I am the smoky hues of peace
I am the brilliant yellow of happiness
I am the sweet rose of mercy
I am the steady scarlet of faith
I am the golden rays of forgiveness
I am the vibrant light of salvation
I am
I am the holy of holies
I am the calm during the storm
I am the sacrifice that brings hope
I am the resounding echo of peace
I am the electric spirit of lightning
I am the translucent beauty of hail
I am the mighty winds of righteousness
I am the fierce clouds of power
I am the glorious rains of grace
I am the rainbow of reconciliation
I am the everlasting gift of love

Run the Eagle Way, was written for my son Sam Thompson because he loved competing in track and running cross-country when he was in middle and high school. It's a concrete style poem in an "E" shape for the Byron Area Eagles. He is autistic (Asperger's) with ADHD and Tourette's, has a sleep disorder called narcolepsy with cataplexy (see [https://rarediseases.org/rare-diseases/narcolepsy/] for more information) and was diagnosed with unidentified chorea (rapid, jerky, involuntary movements [see https://medical-dictionary.thefreedictionary.com/chorea] for more information.) He also has a unique genetic anomaly. We fight and experience these battles daily, learning strength and patience. He discovered running created sunny moments that offset difficult days.

Run the Eagle Way

Eagle pride ascending like clouds at the start line
Run the Eagle way, proudly gliding fast and sure
Take off swift
Arms in flight
Courageously
Feet Advance
Quickly Eagles
Times to beat
Over the fields
Wooded trails
Around lakes
Climbing hills
Through paths
Run the Eagle way sweet rhythm lifting your spirit
Float on feathery wings majestic, resolute and free
Take off swift
Arms in flight
Baton in hand
Courageously
Over hurdles
Circling inside
Painted lines
Quickly Eagle
Close that gap
Time to sprint
Crowd cheers
Beat those wings valiantly show your Eagle pride
Tower to the ground hearts won at the finish line

Faith in Jesus gives me strength. It takes me on a journey toward sunlight, guided by God's grace. Honestly, I still get overwhelmed at times, while I travel through bumpy parts in life that try to jolt me away from God's gift of hope. It remains tough seeing Sam struggle. As he works toward managing one condition, another has manifested or worsened. I express this in these free verse poems, *Trust in Jesus, Army in Spring* and *Waiting in the Doctor's Office.*

Trust in Jesus

A spring of hope
  Gives birth to tulip rows
  Peeking out from the dirt

After spring storms
  Melt away winter's snow
  Flowers open knowing

The sun welcomes them
  Faithful they rise
  Bearing cups full of life

Army in Spring

April marches in with
  Dull-sounding spring rains
Heavy and steady
  Soaking the Earth
Beating with our hearts
  Lulling battered senses
Healing winter-weary bodies
  Tired with sleepy eyes
Waiting to see plants
  Shooting from the ground
Green hues abundant

Opening on branches
Once fallen soldiers
  Coming back redeemed
Sun saluting proudly
  Against applauding sky
God's artistic plan
  Assuring us life
May grow again
  Returning to glory

Waiting in Doctor's Offices

Fake pretty flowers
Covered in forgotten dust
Trapped by small vases
Sitting by dirty glass panes
Sheltered from the stubborn winter air
Loitering miserably outside along
Useless muddy snow piles
Chipping away at my heart

Token Sunny Skies over
Dewy spring blossoms
Painted in generic gold frames
Hanging on dull gray walls
Covered by mirrored armor
Protecting pictures from
Reflections of gray clouds
Pouring into office windows

Sorry frayed carpet slowly
Battered by rips and stains displaying
Trophies of a well-worn life
Trampled by children who wait
Playing and laughing showing
Carefree joy and sincerity
Illuminating the dismal room
Reminding me to smile

Joyous times in my life mix alongside loneliness and emptiness. I lost some family and friends recently. Weaving my heartache with beautiful memories across poetry heals me. I mix them like the colors in the red morning sky. My inspiration for these next free verse poems comes from the strength and hope I have in Jesus.

I love reminiscing about walks along the lake with my dad, Oren Walther. I sensed his spirit and composed, *Sweet Blue Water*. My mother-in-law, Joyce Thompson, loved her kitchen. She cooked memorable holiday meals there and always took breaks to feed the birds, in *Grammy's Kitchen*. Patty Paris loved cheering for her children at track and cross-country meets, inspiring *Patty's Song*. Our neighbor, Al Sundrla, loved hosting campfire get-togethers, inspiring *The Campfire Way*. His kindness measured out his great heart and faith. *Amazing Animals,* was penned in memory of my neighbor, Dale Cudworth. I admired how he cared about animals as well as how much he loved his family and friends. *Rainbow Top Promenade,* was inspired by the many naps I took with my cat, Bo, on the recliner.

Sweet Blue Water

Dear sweet blue water
Rolling waves around boats
Foamy crowns dance on my feet
Playing poetry freely upon the
Warm sandy beach

You sing to my soul
Whistling a melody of
Crisp breezes across my hair
Spreading out like a harp
Rich sounds brush memories

Your spirit plays music

Plucking waves along my ankles
Tiny fish kiss my toes
Walking around lily pads
Frogs croak resonating joy

Swans dance with us
Fluttering feathers wagging tails
Silly like I remember them
Laughing I turn and see
Your footprints next to me

Trees hug God's sun
Electrifying branches gleaming gold
Sunrays piercing through
Making colors between branches
Stain glass light shows

Rippled water reflecting your spirit
Resting patterns in zigzags
My star and beacon
Dropping with one last wink
Sweetly into the deep blue water

Grammy's Kitchen

Grammy loved telling stories
Across the kitchen counter
Full of sass and a touch of sweet
Roasting tales, baking laughter

She earned the nickname
Fireball Fultz
Her fast softball pitches
Striking every batter out

She could dance any waltz,
Jitterbug, jig, electric slide
Winning every contest
With a dynamite smile

She made her rowdy boys
Go to church and school wearing
Trench coats and umbrellas
Their hair looking perfect too

They hated wearing suits so much
And one son grabbed her hat
It sailed three pews over
Landing onto a gentleman's lap
Once a month she played the slots
Always lucky at the casino
Pleased when she hit it big
Saving to do a kitchen remodel

We always took a break
Looking out the kitchen window
At birds and squirrels eating
Nuts and meticulously cut bread

Today, we spotted a cardinal
Tapping on the windowpane
It's an angel from heaven
Laughing and telling stories

Patty's Song

Winds blew harsh
When you died
Clouds rolled in dark and grim
Water rained thick and hard
Running from our eyes
Heavy puddles eating our souls
Cheeks hot and wet
Sobs thundering pain
Booming like broken drums
Hearts trapped in shattered notes

Sweet and calm your spirit lifted in

Whistling your soulful tune
Relaxing our sorrow
Tears become prayers and dreams
Weary and numb we stepped outside
Your laughter dripping into puddles
Smells of rain comforted us
Lingering rich like a loving smile
Warm sun-rays hugged us
Returning joy to ripped souls

Soft breezes fanned across
Peace kissing on our cheeks
Soothed we laced our shoes and stretched
Knowing you wanted us to race again
Our soles striking the ground
Beating rhythms from your heart
Shadows followed us as we soared
Dancing and lifting our feet
Your eyes portraying the bright sun
Twinkling always as we run

The Campfire Way

A kind soul lived the campfire way
His fire blazed generously
Admirable heart twisting flames of
Noble faith never burning out
Celebrating we circle our chairs
Enjoying nature's repartee

Logs set in a tent-like array
Fire roaring warmly
Twigs trilling calmly
Colors spewing at the night sky
Orange-red blazes dancing high
Starry lights winking at us bright

I Look up and see a ring of angels
Sitting by a fire radiant divine
Bright strobes light heaven's night sky

Surpassing human fantasy
Fire blazes drawing colors from
Vibrant logs burning eternal

Trees dancing under the moonlight
Beautiful branches painting a show
Eternal stellar fireworks displaying
Sweet blessings bursting high
Shooting arrows into heaven
Forever celebrating with you

Amazing Animals

Amazing animals sing this song
Let's praise God, march along
Stomp up the ramp in pairs
Flap your arms through the air
Welcome aboard you belong in
Noah's amazing animal ark

Roar   Trumpet   Crow
Wild voices loud and proud
Booming   Infinite   Noisy
Silly animal sounds
Tweet   Quack   Honk

Meow   Purr   Hiss
Anchors aweigh
Whinny   Neigh   Bray
Turn about and say
Ruff   Yap   Bark

Croak   Growl   Ribbit
Noisy sounds echo back
Honk   Trumpet   Quack
God's amazing animal pack
Ooh-ooh-ah-ah

Hoot   Whistle   Squeak
The rain lasts forty days
Gobble   Cluck   Crow
Fierce winds and rolling waves
Ca-caw   Peep   Coo

Float over the flooded earth
Feed and water each animal pair
Please guard with loving care
Cradle them gentle and nice
Majestic wolves and soft wooly sheep
Kingly lions and small furry mice

Neigh   Baa-Baa   Oink
Storm clouds clear out
Ooh-ooh-ah-ah
Climb on deck and look about
Honk   Trumpet   Quack

Chirp   Hoot   Tweet
Sing melodies sweet
Hoot   Whistle   Squeak
Sun playing out musical beats
Meow   Purr   Hiss

Caw   Twitter   Coo
A dove an olive leaf for you
Cock-a-doodle-doo
Noah's ark lands with our animal crew
Oink   Baa   Moo

Ruff   Yap   Bark
Amazing animals shout
Booming   Infinite   Loud
Praising God faithfully
Roar   Quack   Honk

God's amazing animal parade
Marching down the mountain grade

Singing silly animal songs
Please follow along
God's promised blessing on display
A rainbow smiling across the sky

Rainbow Top Promenade

Listen, as deep thunder rolls
Like a ball of yarn
Swish, her proud tail strikes
As she purrs and rumbles
Hush, rain slinks down
Stealth with catlike feet

My quilt feels plush
My book becomes heavy
My cat jumps into my lap
My cheeks get whisker kisses

Stroke, stroking, her back gentle
She lies on my tummy
Purr, purring, we're lulled into sleep
Our eyes grow dream sprinkles

Boom, booming, we hear thunder jolts
I land four-pawed on a jagged bolt
Hiss, wiggle, a tail forms on my back
Whiskers pointed, I sail and float

My fur gets soaked heavy and cold
My four legs are pelted by hail
My dream plays out in a gigantic raindrop
My bolt rides up toward a rainbow top

Slide, slide along the prism arc
Leaving behind fiery sparks
Jump, jump off cottony clouds
Up through the heavenly stars

Twitch, twitching, my tail gleefully
Angels playing a concert for me
Mrowr, mrewr, I croon in symphony
Gold specks cascading around me

My arms hug a fluffy cloud
My life is baptized floating through faith
My cloud morphs into feline fur
My cat joins me through starry skies

Purr, weary eyes flutter and stir
We enjoy cuddle time
Hush, the storm pitters out
My fingers pet her cottony coat
Look, a twinkle in her eyes
As she winks at me sleepily

Springtime hope comes from the patience I learn while muddling through winter's tribulations. In *Around Nature's Circle*, after harsh winters, spring blazes brilliant flowers. Showy sunsets create shadows of the next winter. This poem repeats the letter "B" starting each line. *Michigan Fool's Spring,* depicts how spring in Michigan requires tenacity to endure many weather changes. There are many red sky mornings in a Michigan spring. This is free verse poetry.

Around Nature's Circle

Bulbs dormant forgotten from flowers past
Buried in withered weeds, mud and dirt
Brown dead mottled leaves covering them
Burrowed under dull, miserable, brown snow piles
Baptismal spring rains are welcome along with
Beaming sun-rays healing the hardened ground
Busy people rake paper-thin leaves and find
Bell-shaped buds waiting to taste the light becoming
Billowy silky blooms popping open displaying
Bountiful robust hues swaying with breezes against
Bold flashy sunsets foreshadowing summer's eve

Michigan Fool's Spring

Warm winds spring in
The first robins are spotted
Wait

White stuff's falling
Everything's snow dotted
Wait

Sun's peeking out
I take off my coat
  Wait

Rain showers
I'm soaked all over
  Wait

Graupel pings
My face stings
  Wait

Record high temperatures
Springtime gestures
  Wait

White stuff blows by
Snow piled two feet high
  Wait

Loud thunderous sounds
My power goes out
  Wait

Everything's covered in ice
I slide into the ditch twice
  Wait

Sleet mixed with flurries
Record low degrees
  Wait

Sun's here
Tropical air
  Wait

White stuff again
My windshield's frozen
  Wait

Wind knocks me off my feet
Rain falls every day this week
    Wait

It's sunny, and then it's not
It's rainy, snowy, clear, and then cloudy

Sleet, ice, and now sun and heat
        Now . . . *Wait!*

Michigan Fool's Spring is over
        It's summer.

Dellie Borton

Dellie Borton grew up and currently lives in Owosso, and has been a member of the Shiawassee Area Writers since 2018. She has been married to her husband Thomas for eleven years, is a homeschooling stay at home mom to their four kids, and is currently writing her first novel entitled Kingdom of Beasts. You can follow her journey on her Facebook page Dellie Writes.

For: Kaleb, Kyle, Katara, and Kenneth

"Weeping may last through the night. But joy comes with the
morning."
Psalms 30:5

Seeds
Planted months ago
When leaves burned red,
The world slowed

Before I knew
Before you stirred
My world the same
Undeterred

The snow, the cold
They soften now,
Rays peaking
Through the clouds

Tickles and flutters
Now I feel
There you are
You are real

Stems so tiny
Pushing through
First, second, third,
And fourth, you too

Your roots, they reach
Stretch and draw
The path still hardened
Tough and raw

You have emerged
I am made new
You came from me

Yet, I came from you

The sun, it glows
Beyond the green
You have stripped me
And wiped me clean

Who I once was
Is gone, she soars
Replaced by one
You have made more

The sky it darkens
Strong and wide
You are so small
Please, please survive

Rain crashes
Wind lashes
Thunder and Lightning
My surface is ashes

Your roots, your force
Never forget
Dig down, lean in
Stay your course

I hold you tight
We reach the light
We made it, we made it
Through the night

My love flows
So proud, so proud
You did it, we did it
You showed me how

I thought I knew
Until there was you
You showed me how

You pushed me through

Tall you grow
Bright you shine
I never guessed
You could be mine

Your blossoms emerge
Pointed, closed
Crimson deep
Perfect, posed

Your blooms open
In the warmth of the sun
I see your true self
My daughter, my sons

You open more
And more each day
My Love, my love
Will never stray

Fighting and surging
The storms will come
They knock you down
You'll want to run

Never give up
But if you do
Know I am there
Always for you

Like the first
Weathered together
I am here
With you forever

Your color, it shines
Through darkest nights

My world, it needs you
Set your sights

Your roots in my soil
I finally see
I thought I held you
No doubt you hold me

My world is alive
I live, I thrive
For now my Love,
You've truly arrived

Melissa Wardwell

"We search the world for a romance worth believing in. One that holds promise of something better. Sadly, we come up short when we look around this world, only find love that is self seeking. My hope in writing romance is that readers will close the book and know that they have seen romance the way it was meant to be. Passionate, unhindered, unconditional, and full of promise"

Melissa Wardwell resides in Owosso, Michigan with her husband Jonathan, three children, a cat, and two pitbulls.

Besides writing, she enjoys reading, having coffee with friends, and spending quality time with her husband kayaking.

Melissa likes to joke about the voices in her head, but in reality, those voices have inspired her to write several romance novels such as *"I Know the Plans"* (a story based in her hometown of Owosso) and *"Finding Hope in Savannah"*. When she is not penning works of fiction, she is busy reviewing books on her blog *Back Porch Reads*.

To see more from Melissa Wardwell, visit www.melissawardwell.com

First Love, Spring Love

They say that it is easy to find love in spring because after the doldrums of winter, your dopamine levels rise as the weather warms and you're outside more. That may be, but I say it also comes from a willingness to let someone new into your life.

I met a boy, one sunny spring day, at the tender age of fifteen. He wasn't what I was looking for in a boyfriend. In fact, I wasn't looking for a boyfriend at all. Surprisingly, I was lost when I saw his school picture hanging on the living room wall. His dark hair, chocolate hazel eyes, and sheepish smile endeared him to me. Something stopped me as I studied his face and whispered in my heart that this boy, who looked much older than me, would be my forever person. I wasn't sure how that could be, but I could see in his eyes that he would be a boy I could trust.

It all started with a babysitting job, a regular way of earning some spending money for a typical teen girl in the 1990s. It wasn't a job I hated, but waking at seven in the morning on a Saturday was not at the top of my list of favorite things to do. I mean, why does the world have to start that early on a weekend? Anyway, the girl was a six-year-old punky little thing that had a love for Garfield the cat and Tweety bird. She fluttered around the house, chirping and laughing. She was an easy child to watch and we had a great time.

Around lunch time that day, a burly six-foot tall man wearing what looked like a security guard uniform, barreled through the front door scaring me and the little girl. He didn't stop to say hello or apologize for his abruptness, instead he charged up the stairs.

"Oh, that's big bro. He's always like that. You'll like him," the little sprite announced as she put her crayon down and hopped down from the kitchen table chair.

A thunder of footsteps echoed as he made his way down the stairs and I watched in wonder as he entered the tiny living room. He must have caught a glimpse of me out of the corner of his eye because he froze in his path. He turned in my direction, his hand stretched out to introduce himself.

"Sorry to scare you. I only have a quick break and need to get back. I'll be done around three. Will you still be here?" His eyes dazzled with interest as he spoke. I will admit that the feeling was mutual.

"I'm here until your mom is out of work," I told him.

"Awesome," he nodded as he hurried out the door.

I recall the knot of anticipation forming in my stomach as he left. It only grew with each glance at the clock. It was the longest three hours of my young life. I tried to fill the time with homework, quirky kids shows, and a game or two with my little charge, but none of it helped.

At last, the time on the clock turned to three. I waited for him to walk through the door. I tried to hide how eager I was by pretending to read a book. He said his hellos as he entered, gave his wild little sister a hug, and went to the kitchen. A large opening between the living room and kitchen made it possible to steal glances at him while he busied around making a sandwich and getting a drink.

"So, you look familiar. Have we met?" he asked as he took a

seat across the room on the couch.

I studied his face trying to conjure up any memories I might have of him. Then one hit. "Actually, we met at the concert at the Lebowski a couple of months ago."

"That's right, you came to the back of the room and said hi to my mom."

As we talked, we discovered that our paths crossed several times over the previous year and that our parents went to school together.

"You always seemed to have a boyfriend every time our paths crossed," he mentioned.

"That's probably why it took a minute to remember you." I pondered if I should divulge the next bit of information when his sister approached him and asked him to get something for her. I decided to leave out that I wasn't dating anyone now and I was definitely paying attention.

"Hey, I need to run to Durand to pick up my papers from the Independent. You and sis want to tag along. You can meet my grandma while we're there." His eyes danced with boyish hope.

"YES!" His sister answered for me as she jumped up and down.

"I guess so. Let me call my mom real quick to let her know."

"Okay. I need to change before we go anyway."

Excitement built as I phoned my mom and informed her what we were doing. Never had I gone anywhere with anyone other than my parents or adult family members. My friends and I were to start driver's training in the summer, so we were still riding the bus to school. This guy had his own vehicle. This was new territory for me.

As we stepped outside, he indicated that his truck was by the curb. This was my first lesson on being slow to judge that I can recall. His baby blue, long box Chevy S-10 truck was riddled with rust holes. The interior was consumed with his bass speaker, wires, and school papers. Apparently he liked the thump of the bass while I preferred country tunes. With us girls standing there, he made quick work of disconnecting the speaker so he could take it and his papers in the house.

Once we were on our way, he and I chatted about school and family as we traveled from Owosso to Durand. His sister chimed in from time to time making sure her presence was acknowledged. It was comfortable and easy to talk to him. My mom's words sounded off in my mind. "If the boy was a girl and would be your best friend, it might be a good idea to snatch him up if he asks. Being friends with your significant other before you become more intimate isn't a bad way to start a life-long relationship."

Rolling into Durand, it was pretty clear that Railroad Days was in full swing. We had to creep through the back way to get to our pick-up point. Dirty looks from pedestrians seemed to tell us that we were intruding on their walking path yet they were the ones jaywalking or walking down the middle of the street. One older couple drove by, giving us a disapproving gaze while shaking their heads. We looked at each other, already communicating with our eyes, questioning the curious behavior. Both of us shrugged our shoulders and smiled at each other over the little blonde head that rested on my shoulder. It was thrilling to know that already, we could communicate without a word spoken.

After we picked up two-county routes worth of newspapers, thus filling the bed of the S-10, he did his best to get us out of town as quick as possible. The more he and I talked, the more I could see the possibility of a relationship.

Pulling into Owosso, he put his arm over the back of the seat behind his sister, his calloused fingers skimming my neck. He tilted his head so he could look at her and me, as well as keep his focus on the road. "How about ice cream?"

His sister went berserk with excitement which made us both smile. There was no way I was about to talk over the squeal of a six-year-old girl. He pulled into the little ice cream shop on the corner of Washington Street and Corunna Avenue, where he bought a hot fudge Sunday for his sister and a strawberry dipped cone for me. We sat at the counter, watching traffic pass by, so he could eat his banana split without fear of making a mess.

Back at the house, he and I chatted some more about church and friends we had in common. It seemed like there was never a limit to our conversation. That was until the time came for him to head out on his route.

"I'd ask you to come along, but I don't think your parents would be okay with that." His hesitance was adorable.

"You're probably right. It was nice talking with you."

"Yeah, same here."

I agreed and wondered if we would ever see each other again or if that little voice from earlier in the day was just a wish.

"So, I was wondering if can I get your number? I like talking to you," his bashful request made my heart melt.

Never had a boy asked me for my number. All the other boys had gotten my number from friends but never asked me directly. It spoke volumes about his character; straightforward, honest, goes after what he wants.

We exchanged numbers and he left. Not long after that, his mom arrived home and my mom picked me up.

Three long days later, he finally called. I sat in the bathroom off the kitchen, the telephone cord stretching across the kitchen and pinched in the door as we monopolized the line for three hours. Again, conversation was easy and with each revelation, a new blossom of affection bloomed. I knew this was different from the other "boyfriends". I couldn't explain it, but the feeling was the most intense I ever experienced and I didn't want to let it go.

By the end of that phone call, he asked me to be his girl. Well, he more or less fumbled through it.

"You know, I like you. I don't know if you feel the same, and you can tell me no if you want, but I just enjoyed the other day and the call, and yeah…"

I couldn't keep my laughter at bay. "Hey, my mom just called for dinner. Hurry and ask so I can say yes and hang up before I get in trouble."

We laughed, he asked, I said yes, and we said our good-byes.

There are days that I long for those simple, spring nights when we would sit on the back porch or in his S-10 truck, watching the stars and talking with each other. Those moments were priceless, and are still the most cherished memories, but now it has been twenty-four years and he still makes my heart melt. Conversation has transitioned from words to looks across the living room. Yet, no matter what life throws our way, I continue to hold on to my first love, my spring love.

Leland Scott

Leland Scott was raised in rural Michigan. He began a military career in the Navy in 1956, serving as an instructor and pursuing a career in drafting. After twenty years of service, he retired and returned to civilian life in Michigan with his wife and four children.

As a civilian, he used his vocational training to follow a trade of drafting and teaching. Working in engineering firms, Leland taught in business meetings and also taught part-time in community college. He then taught at Baker College for 22 years. He now maintains a part-time business designing homes.

Leland began writing while in the Navy, writing poetry of his experiences. He entered a navy-wide essay contest with one of his poems, *What is an American,* and was awarded the winner of the Freedom Foundation award and George Washington Medal.

While faculty at Baker College; Leland was awarded the Instructor of the Year award. He was also named the College Poet Laureate and wrote for a monthly poetry column in the college paper.

Leland continues to write poetry, music, and short stories, and has published three books: *Pangatango's Secrets, Special Moments in Poetry, BASIC DRAFT-ING a manual for beginning drafters,* and is a contributor author to the published book, *Winter in the Mitten.*

Leland received an MBA at Baker College, a Bachelor's degree from John Wesley College , a Vocational Education Teaching Certificate from the University of Maryland, Teaching Certificate from the U. S. Navy, and diplomas from two Navy Drafting schools. Leland also attended William and Mary College, Old Dominion College, and Lansing Community College.

Decisions

Lance hadn't intended to stay in Richland. He was just passing through. He had spent one day and a night there in December. He had left town only to turn around and return. Something about the people he had met intrigued him. Joan had been one of those people.

He stayed to enjoy Christmas with the whole town. The Christmas Festival had been fun, and he had been urged to stay a while longer. He began to feel 'attached'.

He was offered a part-time job at the marina drawing from his experience as an electrician in the Navy, found an apartment and moved in. Joan had become a fun companion; all was good, but, still, he was uncertain. He had been there four months - four months . . . was it time? Lance was wondering if he should move on. He still had a desire to see the country.

It was Easter weekend, but the marina was busy. Lance had spent Saturday morning there and was walking home as he often did; it was less than a mile and a warm spring day. The sun was shining and the melting snow caused rivulets of water to run along the edge of the road. Lance was lost in thought, enjoying the whole atmosphere. He spotted a dandelion just opening in a patch of grass near the edge of the road, and stooped to pick it. As he twirled it between his fingers like a tiny parasol, memories of a time long ago rushed into his mind.

Just then, Joan's familiar yellow jeep splashed to a stop beside him.

"Lance! I almost ran over you! I can tell you are off in La La Land. What are you thinking about?" she asked. "Did you forget that we're supposed to help out at the school for the sunrise service?"

"I guess I did! I just picked this dandelion and was wondering if I should take my shoes off." He grinned.

"WHAT? What are you talking about?"

"Sorry, long story."

"Well, keep your shoes on, climb in, and you can tell me all about it on the way to the school. I'm glad I found you."

"Me too."

"Well, no problem, we're ok now. I want to hear more about this shoes thing. You can tell me while we move chairs."

"It's nothing, just an old memory that I had forgotten til' I saw this dandelion," he explained as he twirled it for her to see.

"Yeah? What's it with the dandelion? Did you pick that for me?" she teased.

"Sure! That's it! It's an Easter bouquet!"

"No, really – what's it all about?"

Lance hesitated, then began to share how that when he was ten years old, he lived with his grandparents on a farm in Michigan. His grandmother had told him that the first dandelion was a sign of summer and when you saw one you could pick it and use it as proof that summer was here and go barefoot.

"That's a neat story! I never heard of that. Maybe after we get done with the chairs, we could both take our shoes off !'"

Lance changed the subject. "Explain this 'Sunrise service' thingy again."

"All of the churches get together and celebrate the resurrection – like when Mary went to the tomb. So we have an outdoor service at sunrise. We use the ball field for the service, so we're taking chairs out and setting them up today to be ready."

"Um, okay, I guess."

At the school, others were already carrying chairs out of the building and setting them up in rows facing a podium in the middle of the field. They followed, joining in the process. As they worked, Joan pressed for more of Lance's story of his summer on the farm.

"I thought you grew up in Chicago."

"I did, but that one summer. . ." He went on to tell of how his mother had lost her job and apartment and he had stayed that summer in Michigan. He told of how different it had been than living in the city and how he learned to do chores and drive the tractor with his Grampa and how they went to church on Sundays and that was when he became a Christian in the little country church.

"Wow! You became a Christian when you were ten years old?" Joan stopped, put her chair down, and gave Lance a big hug. "You never told me about any of that!"

"Well, it was a long time ago. I never learned much about 'religion', but yes, I'm a Christian. Grampa gave me a Bible. I still have it. You've seen it at church on Sundays - I try to read it, but don't understand it all. We never went to church in Chicago, but I went to services on the ship in the Navy - and I met some missionaries once."

Lance became quiet, but when the last chair was in place, Joan suggested that they find some place to talk. She could tell that Lance was feeling nostalgic and wanted to give him a chance to let it out. She drove to a little park near the river and led him to a bench where they sat down.

"Where's that dandelion?" she asked with a sly little smile as she reached down and took off her shoes and socks, settling her bare feet into the cold grass. "There. Now, take your shoes off and tell me more about your life," she challenged. "I've known you for four months and you've never told me much about yourself."

Lance hesitated, but he had started the whole thing, so he sheepishly kicked off his shoes and laughed. "There's not much to tell. I'm sorry to have said all that I did."

"No! no. I am glad you did. I want to hear more about your summer on that farm. I want to hear about your Navy life and about your Bible."

"Like I said, there isn't much to tell. When I lived on the farm, it was with my Grampa and Gramma. It was the best summer of my life. I loved learning from them. I really liked going to their church. I'd never been to church before. Mom taught me to say my prayers, but those were just words. The church prayers were different. And I liked the preaching! One Sunday I asked Jesus to come into my heart and Grampa gave me that Bible and told me to keep it and read it every day. I've tried to do that, even in the Navy.

"I joined the Navy after high school and have never been back there. I have been thinking that maybe I should go visit my Grampa and Gramma again – if they are still there."

"You don't know?"

"No, I didn't keep in contact much. I saw them at my mom's funeral, but that was all so rushed. I never got to talk to them. My leave was too short. The ship happened to be in port in San Diego when Mom died. I got a chance to fly home just in time for the funeral and then back again before I had to go back to sea. It was all too sudden."

"That must have been hard.."

They sat silent for a moment, then, "Tell me more about your navy life and the missionaries you met!" Joan said excitedly, wanting to learn more about Lance while he was in the mood to talk.

"Well, there isn't much to tell. After I got out of boot camp, I went to electrician's school and then to a ship on the West Coast and that is about it. At the end of my enlistment, I got transferred to Norfolk and discharged there."

"And the missionaries? How did you meet missionaries in the Navy?"

"Oh! My ship went to Guam for a while for some repairs, and I went to a little church there, and met a couple that traveled to islands to preach to natives. They asked me if I would like to go with them for a few days on one of their trips. I got leave and went. It was a neat experience."

"Really? Where did you go?"

"Oh, we flew to a few little islands. We stayed for like a half a day at each place, and spent nights with local people. The missionaries mostly just went to visit people where they had preached, and they also preached a couple of times in the native's churches. I didn't do anything but go along."

"Wow, that sounds exciting!"

"Yeah, it was more exciting than anything else I did in the Navy."

"I guess the Navy wasn't exciting?"

"Not really – we didn't go to war or nothin." He laughed.

"I am glad you settled here," Joan ventured. "And I'm glad you finally shared about your Grampa and Gramma. You have to tell me more about that summer." She said as she slipped her shoes back on.

"Yeah, sure, maybe sometime." He rose, pushed his feet into his shoes, and reached for her hand.

"I'll pick you up in the morning," Joan said as she dropped Lance off at his apartment. "Don't forget!" She teased, and drove off.

The sunrise service was just as Joan had described. The whole town seemed to be there, wrapped in coats against the chilly air. Lance and Joan sat together with her parents on the chairs they had set up the day before. The sun had, indeed, just risen, spreading a special glow in a brightening sky. The leader read the account of

tom."

Joan read the first aloud:

> *Life is made for living*
> *Live it fully every day*
> *Rise up with the dawning*
> *Let no moment get away*
> *Be careful in your footsteps*
> *Let wisdom guide your way*
> *Let your speech be always pleasant*
> *Choose every word you say*
> *Look to all of nature*
> *it is God's gift to you*
> *He gave it for your pleasure*
> *His handiwork to view*
> *Listen to the singing*
> *Of the tiny sparrow's song*
> *He sings his song to heaven*
> *happily chirping all day long*

And then, the second:

> *Just beyond a distant hill*
> *there's a place with pastures green*
> *where the cattle graze their fill*
> *beside a sparkling stream*
> *The fences all are straight*

'round fields of golden grain

The corn is green and tall

refreshed from a recent rain

The barns are spotless clean

there's the smell of fresh cut hay

In the garden by the house

happy children laugh and play

The sky is brightest blue

with clouds of purest white

And when the sun goes down

moonlight floods the night

Beyond that far-off hill

it's a scene of peaceful bliss

It's easy to believe

that Heaven's just like this

Joan became quiet for a moment, as she handed the box back to Lance, then spoke. "Lance" She said, "You have to go back!"

"Go back? What do you mean? Where?"

"To Michigan, to your family!"

"I don't think so. It's too complicated. They were my dad's parents. I never knew my dad. There was some kind of bad blood that no one ever told me. I don't want to know."

"But they are your grandparents – you liked them; they liked you … You can't just live with a memory. You have to go back."

Lance shrugged it off and put the Bible away. "Maybe sometime."

The next morning, Lance drove to the gas station, parked, and found Joan working on a car in the garage. Sensing something unusual, she greeted him expectantly.

"I've decided that you were right," he began. "I have been thinking all night and you were right." He stood for a moment, then announced, "I am going to Michigan." He waited for a moment, then added, "You wanna go along?"

Connie LaMee

Connie LaMee is a retired preschool teacher from Congregational Child Development Center and St. Joseph Child Care Services. She received her Child Development Associates Degree from Lansing Community College. Her inspiration for writing comes from the true authors of children. Connie kept a collection of the crazy, wonderful, funny and precious things that kids would say in her classroom and created a scrapbook along with photos to present to every child at the end of each year.

"Grammy" rings music to her ears from her six grandchildren. She continues to keep a journal of their stories. Connie resides in Owosso, Michigan with her husband, Gary. They have two adult children.

God is good! After forty years, Connie was reunited with a SAW member, Brenda Stroub, who sparked her interest in this group of inspiring writers and became a member in October 2018.

Heart Melt Moments (1)

It was a warm spring day, perfect for ice cream. I had given my three-year-old grandson, Seth, a coupon for a free cone from McDonald's a few days before. Since Seth's parents both work, I was blessed to care for him. On this particular day, Seth asked if we could go to McDonald's to redeem his coupon. I asked Seth if he had any money. He ran to his room, came out waving a piece of paper in his hand and said "I don't need money, I have a coupon." So, off to McDonald's we went.

When we arrived, Seth marched to the counter. He handed his paper to the cashier and said "I have a coupon for a free cone. Does ice cream come in it?"

Heart Melt Moments (2)

My favorite part of spring is planting our garden with our grandchildren. Once the garden is planted, my husband and I walk through the garden every day to see the miraculous seeds grow into amazing foods with vibrant rainbow colors, shapes and sizes. Tesa and Beka eagerly race to the garden to search for luscious, red cherry tomatoes as they can hardly wait to devour them.

Quite often the girls spend the night after a fun-filled day at Grammy and Grandpa's. At bedtime we read, tell stories and sing. One night they lay beside me very quietly. I began singing "I come to the garden alone while the dew is still on the roses-and the voice I hear-falling on my ear-the Son of God discloses-and he walks with me and He talks with me and He tells me I am His own-and the joy we share as we tarry there none other has ever known." Tesa faintly whispered "That's a very pretty song." I continued singing "He speaks and the sound of His voice is so sweet the birds hush their singing-and the melody that He gave to me within my heart is ringing.

Beka softly interrupted and said "I know who you are talking about." I responded "who?" She answered "Grandpa, because he always goes for walks with you in the garden and he talks nice to you." I cried tears of joy for such a perfect picture as she related to Grandpa in the portrayal of Jesus.

Heart Melt Moments (3)

After church one spring day, our four-year-old grandson, Zane and his siblings were singing a song about God's creation. Zane began naming all the things that apply to that song, then asked me if Jesus helped God make everything. I explained that Jesus is God's son. Zane then asked about heaven. I shared with him that we must pray and ask Jesus to forgive us of our sin, then accept him into our heart. When we do this, we will go to heaven to live with Jesus forever. Zane looked at me and said, "I want to do that! I always wanted to see Jesus, but no one would ever lift me high enough!"

Tenderhearted Tesa and Beka

Little girls radiate the Jesus glow
They spread light to everyone they know
In tune with sadness, joy or sorrow
Offering their childlike hope for tomorrow.

Music and dance is their gift from above
Sharing life with everyone they love
Dance recitals in their spring attire
Little girls, so cute to admire.

The Jesus glow is forever in their hearts
Because of a decision right from the start
To believe in Jesus, to love and to pray
And follow Him each step of the way.

Little girls at the age of five
Proclaim good news, Jesus is alive!
Thank you Jesus for my grand twins
May they be a blessing again and again.

Song for the King

Eight eager children ran down the stairs
raced to the table to pull out a chair
A basket with candy, an outfit too
What could be better than something brand new!

Wearing new clothes to church we bring
A song as an offering for Jesus the King.
The King who wore a thorny crown
As in the song "…As The Sun Went Down."

God's word was read, the preacher spoke
A worshipful day with such beautiful folk.

Mother announced that our home would feed
any and all of those in need.
Homemade noodles and chicken dinner
always made our home a winner.

Mrs. May was a widow who always came
And brought her dog, "Wee sing" was his name.
With anticipation we waited to sing
Around the piano for our Savior and King!

Hand in Hand

Gnarled, ancient cypress trees shade the long winding road
That leads to Kiawah Island
Anticipation of searching for alligators in the lagoons and ponds
On the swampy banks of Kiawah Island
Strolling the majestic shoreline hand in hand with my love
Exploring the scenic Kiawah Island
Glimpses of dolphins captivate with their charm
In the Atlantic Ocean on Kiawah Island
World Class golf courses set the tone for a
Challenging game on Kiawah Island
A private villa in a secluded corner
With such tranquility on Kiawah Island
A screened-in porch with a picturesque scene
Paints the empty canvas of springtime
On Kiawah Island

From Fear to Love

Dobermans, Pit Bulls, Chihuahuas all knew
They gave me a fear I'd grown accustomed to.
Long prayer walks down the road and back
The vicious dogs looked ready to attack.

I moved swiftly by their territory
Would I soon be entering into God's glory?
Day after day I began my routine
I carried a stick but not to be mean.

In the spring my son Joel, returned from the Navy
With an Australian Healer, I exclaimed "Are you crazy?"
The tan and white dog was named Eli
What is happening? I wondered "why?"

Eli seemed frightened just like me
His fear was with people, NOW I could see.
It didn't take long for us to bond
Eli and I whispered our fear to God.

We walked and walked eight miles a day
We grew close together as we would pray.
Eli and I are very best friends
My heart changed from fear to love in the end.

Jason Bullard

Jason Bullard is a graduate from Long Ridge Writers Group. He has written a short story called *The Long walk in* the *Storyteller* magazine January 2015 issue. His debut book of short stories is called *Strange Tales Book One*. He enjoys writing every day and reads as much as possible. His passion for creative writing at an early age. He likes to write fiction that deals with thriller, mystery, and horror. Jason has been a member of Shiawassee Area Writers for over a year. He has a website *bullard.xyz*. Connect him at his email *jasonbullard41@gmail.com*. Jason lives in Michigan.

Spring Forever

A tiny voice asked, "Do you need any help?"

David jumped a little bit and turned around to see a girl with long black hair. She had on a yellow sun dress. He guessed her age must have been around twelve-years-old. A smile came across his face as he stood up. "Well, I could use an extra pair of hands to pull these weeds out of my garden. That is, if you don't mind getting dirty."

The little girl laughed at him. "Hi, my name is Lily Cruise."

"Hi, I am David Hardy." He stretched out his hand.

Lily took his hand and gave it a hard shake. David laughed to himself. Getting on their knees they both started the process of pulling the tangled weeds. After a while, David began to get thirsty.

"I am going to get a drink. I'll be right back." David made his way to the kitchen. Retrieving a jug of fresh lemonade from the refrigerator, he poured the lemonade in two cups. It didn't take long to return outside. David looked around, but Lily was nowhere to be seen. But now, brightly colored flowers brightened the garden.

David's mother passed away a few years ago and the garden was her pride and joy. His mother was always on his mind, he mentioned it to Lily a few times about her passing. He wanted to make sure he kept it up and looking good.

For weeks straight, she kept disappearing. David let Lily help him; she then would just disappear. Different thoughts started to seep into his mind. The fact he brought up his dead mother might have scared her. The way his mother loved her garden and he talked about it all the time. It could also be when he tried to show her how to maintain the garden. David worked with her for a few hours then excused himself. He went to hide, so he could see what she might do. Lily looked around then started to walk away towards the woods by the cabin. As she entered, he didn't hesitate to follow her.

David squinted through the haze of insects that kept biting his sweating legs. The sun couldn't shine through the massive trees overhead. The sun did, however, cast shadows throughout the woods. David kept looking all around, especially behind. Finally seeing an opening in the woods, he shook his head in disbelief.

David saw a woman by a cabin doing some painting on a canvas. He made his way over to the woman to see if she had seen the little girl. This must have been his new neighbor, and she looked friendly enough. The woman looked at him, and he flashed her a nervous grin.

"Hi there."

The woman waved but didn't say anything.

David cleared his throat. "I live in a cabin on the other side of the woods. My parents left it to me. I was wondering if you saw a little girl with dark hair? She was helping me in my garden and keeps disappearing on me."

The woman just stared at David. A look of sadness crept in her eyes. He thought maybe something was wrong about with what he said. David looked around the area to see if maybe he missed something. It did bother him that she was almost in tears. The woman wasn't that far away so he stepped a little closer to comfort her.

The woman started to talk. "The only little girl with dark hair I know is my daughter."

This made him smile; he was going to meet her mother. Smiling like that in front of her might have seemed creepy. He was, after all, a stranger. David walked up to her with his hand outstretched. The woman hesitated, but did finally shake his hand. This made him wonder if he did something wrong.

"I would like to thank your daughter for her help in my garden. Is it okay to see her?"

"Sir, I don't know what game you are playing, but my daughter is dead. We buried her in my flower garden."

David saw the woman point by the far side of the cabin. There was a beautiful flower garden. He didn't understand what was going on. How could she appear in his garden if she had died?

"I am looking for a girl named Lily Cruise."

"Mister, stop trying to scare me. Are you joking? That was my daughter's name."

David couldn't believe what she was telling him. There was no way this could be the same little girl. He had to go the flower garden to see for himself. David turned and headed to it as the woman screamed. "Get out of there!" He didn't pay any attention to her screams.

The flower garden was breathtaking. The flowers were all in bloom, just like his garden. The colors ranged from yellow, red, orange and dark purple. David stood on the edge of the flower garden. In the center stood a tombstone. Lily's picture was on the top of it. Engraved in big letters it read, *I will live in Spring Forever.*

David fell to his knees. He didn't want to be like his mother who saw ghosts. It had driven her mad. His heartbeat raced, pulsating through his head like a pounding drum. The events of the past few weeks suddenly grew vivid. He screamed. The next thing David realized, three police officers were dragging him away. He kept screaming, "Don't take me away. I know what I saw, she was real. You have to believe me."

David realized that it was too late for him as he sat in the back of the police car. The police wouldn't listen to him. He heard one call him crazy. David looked to his left and saw Lily sitting next to him with an eerie smile. A scream started to come but she put her hand over his mouth. Lily leaned in whispering to him, "You are mine."

Wildflowers

Bruce was running toward Denny at full speed. Denny didn't know what to think. He had never seen Bruce look so scared. The echo of Bruce's shoes pounded off the blacktop. As Bruce got closer, Denny stayed perfectly still.

"Denny run!"

Denny blinked a couple of times, the scene behind Bruce seemed unreal. Two large hedges were scraping across the blacktop. Their long branches were reaching out to grab them. He could have sworn he saw large teeth moving within the green leaves.

Denny turned and began running behind Bruce toward an old school. Something slashed at Denny's leg, the pain caused him to cry out. There was no way he would turn around to look. Denny kept the pain to himself as they reached the school building. A few windows were broken and they decided to climb in through one to get inside.

Denny thought it was safe enough to look at his leg when they got in. A large cut slashed his left calf. The wound already looked infected, with green ooze. It spilled from it and ran down his calf. He figured the hedges had some kind of poison on their branches, to cause such an instant infection. The burning sensation crept up his leg toward his thigh. He wanted to find a place to relax his leg.

An old stool sat against the wall on the far side of the room. Denny hobbled over to it. The pain increased, which caused him to cry out. He didn't know how much more his body could take.

"Denny, what's wrong?"

"I am in a lot of pain. It hurts so bad."

Denny saw Bruce leave the room. A terrible thought came to him that Bruce might be leaving him. He didn't want to be alone in this nightmare. The pain shot through his whole body which caused him to lose balance, falling to the floor.

Denny laid on the floor staring at the ceiling. Tears started to flow down his face. Bruce appeared above him with something in his hand. Denny felt his body being rolled over.

"This might hurt Denny, take a deep breath."

Denny cried out in pain, grabbing on to the side of his face. He couldn't believe how much it hurt. The next thing he heard was a sizzling sound, like someone cooking hamburger on the stove in a frying pan.

"All right Denny, I think I did the best I can."

"What…was that stuff?" Denny clenched his jaw.

"It is peroxide. I…I found it."

Denny wanted to be grateful to his best friend, but it didn't take the pain away. Sweat started to run down his forehead. All that pain made his adrenaline go crazy. He looked up in time at the broken window to see a flower with white and red petals go by.

"Bruce, did you see that?"

Denny looked concerned at his friend who was staring intently at the broken window. It took a few minutes, but he finally got Bruce's attention.

"Sorry, I just wanted to make sure those flowers didn't get in," Bruce said with trembling lips

Denny grabbed on to Bruce's arm to stand. The pain came in

spurts, but it didn't stop him from getting up. Leaning on his friend to relieve some pressure off his leg, they both walked to the stool. Looking at each other, they didn't know what to do next. Denny finally looked around and noticed a portable radio on a shelf. He pointed over to it so Bruce would go get it.

As Bruce turned it on, a DJ started to talk. *"This is an emergency hour. Please listen and be prepared. I know this sounds like fantasy. All plant life is taking over the world. This is only April, and I don't know if we can hold on. Lilac bushes attacked my family and killed them all. Use fire to kill them if you must. I want everyone to take cover and be safe."*

Denny had Bruce shut off the radio. To hear about it from someone else made it even more real. They were trapped in the school because of his injury. There was no way he could outrun the plant life. They were lucky to get away from the hedges. For now, they were in a safe place.

Time seemed to drag on, Bruce checked the window to see if it was safe to make a run for it. Denny could see the flowers near the window. By the time he tried to warn Bruce, the flowers started to shoot pollen. The window started to melt like acid had touched it. Bruce jumped back. This scared Denny, causing him to fall backwards.

The hard concrete floor came up to meet him. His head bounced a couple of times. Spots floated above him, pain shooting to his head. Denny didn't want to move anymore.

"Denny, are you okay?"

To answer, he had to muster the strength. "I feel okay. My head hurts."

Denny finally managed to get up into a sitting position. He looked at Bruce. "I want you to go get help. If we both stay, we will die."

Bruce looked sad. This didn't make Denny feel any better. He knew what was happening next. Bruce was getting ready to leave. The only hope he had was if Bruce got help. Laying on the cold floor, he hoped and prayed no plants would break in.

Denny sat alone now, straining his ears to listen to every sound. It started to get dark and he looked constantly around the room. If the flowers didn't get him a heart attack might. There was always a chance a bush or hedge would find a way to get inside. His stomach started to growl. Now a new problem-- starvation; his eyelids started to get heavy.

The sunlight streamed through the broken window woke Denny. He was shocked that he'd fallen asleep. Some scratching sounds made him look at the door. In the doorway were a line of green bushes. Tears started to come down Denny's face as he whispered, "No."

This didn't stop them for coming at him. The sounds of broken bones, screams of pain, and the spatter of blood. The bushes won, enjoying their fresh kill. The plant life would soon be taking over the world.

Denny woke up in a cold sweat and stared at his surroundings. He hurried out of bed to look out the window. The brushes were still there in the yard. They needed to still be trimmed. He laughed to himself realizing that it must have all been a dream.

Gracelyn Keys

Pamela McKee is a children's author and a mental wellness advocate. She is working on writing and illustrating several picture books on various mental health topics to help children understand more about these challenges. She is a member of the Shiawassee Area Writers Group and Society of Children's Book Writers and Illustrators. She writes children's books under the pen name of **Gracelyn Keys**. Her first book is titled, *Knock, Knock, Who's There, Bear? A Story About Embracing Bipolar Disorder*. Her Facebook page can be found at Gracelyn-KeysAuthor.

She has a bachelor's degree from the University of Michigan in clinical community psychology and a master's degree in business administration from Central Michigan University. She worked in the human services area for over twenty-five years. She resides in Byron, Michigan, with her husband, Bob, and Dachshund dog, Bruiser, and thirteen chickens. She has three adult married children and ten grandchildren. She and her husband love vacationing on the Straits of Mackinac.

Spring on the Straits of Mackinac

Friday night is date night in the car for my husband and me, while we travel to our cottage for a fun-filled spring weekend. That means a four-hour drive to our little piece of paradise on the Straits of Mackinac, which is where Lake Huron and Lake Michigan meet in northern Michigan between the lower and upper peninsula. Our cottage is small but the view is large, overlooking Mackinac Island and the Mackinac Bridge. Our date night consists of good country music in the car or listening to whatever game is broadcasting on the radio, along with a stop at one of our favorite fast food places along the way.

Even our dog, Bru, short for Bruiser, gets his little wiener dog tail moving so fast when he knows we are getting ready to pack up the truck to head north. As soon as his dog crate is loaded up in our blue Chevy truck, Bru begs to get up into it. He tries to help by placing his front paws on the step up into the truck and jumping into his crate. It's hilarious to watch this long, black Dachshund with his super short legs trying to do his part. He usually rides along well the entire trip, rarely getting out until we reach the cottage.

Last spring, in April, we went up for our usual weekend. Beyond Gaylord, traveling I-75 north, we feel we're almost to our home away from home as we see the billboards for the ferries to Mackinac Island. Soon we passed the exit for Sea Shell City, clearly visible from the highway. I always think back to my younger years when we would tell the kids to say Sea Shell City really fast ten times, and without fail, they would crack up laughing while replacing the "c" in city with an "sh". Then after a few more miles we saw it…the bridge.

Approaching Mackinaw City, topping a hill, we see the magnificent Mackinac Bridge. It's an amazing sight each and every time we see it. This five-mile-long suspension bridge connecting the two parts of Michigan is just spectacular to see at night and is a favorite part of our date night. There are red blinking lights on top of the bridge's two towers with colorful lights that align the cables spanning the bridge leading to the towers. Ice and snow still cover the Great Lakes, but we also know we'll arrive soon to our little cottage on the Straits.

As we near Mackinaw City, and my husband and I start to excitedly chatter about the bridge, Bru awakens and starts to stretch and yawn. He knows we will be getting out of the truck soon.

Our cottage has been a work in progress for almost eight years. We were fortunate enough to find it for sale in the winter. When you've been married and have owned the same house for over thirty years, it's a relief to have paid off that mortgage. Purchasing a vacation home, we incurred another mortgage. But it's a different kind of feeling paying down a mortgage for a vacation home. For us, it feels like paying for a legacy for future generations.

Our cottage was built in the 1950's, around the same time as the Mackinac Bridge. It is made of red brick sitting on a slab foundation. Even the walls inside are brick. This sturdy but smaller vintage cottage has an open concept living room, dining room and kitchen. It has large windows to look out across the lake and nearby islands, which include Mackinac, Round and Bois Blanc Islands. There are three small bedrooms and a bathroom. The cottage has been nicely renovated with modern day amenities but still holds that vintage charm of yesteryear.

Our cottage has a small, black, wood burning stove, along with floor heating under the tiled floor throughout the cottage. There is no furnace, although we have plans for adding a furnace one day. Our cottage would be considered a summer seasonal home.

We love the outdoors, and once the cottage is winterized and the water is turned off for the season, we consider it cottage camping when traveling north for a weekend. We bring in water for cooking, showers and toilet use. Everything else is electric and works standard.

We figured out we could take a shower using a solar camping shower, instead of heading to a hotel. We hang it in the ceiling of the shower and add hot water from the stove, while we stand in a small plastic tub inside the shower. It takes a little more effort to take a camping shower, but it is well worth it to have a hot shower at the cottage. It feels like a luxury, we can't do without.

In early spring, Mackinaw City weather feels like winter. There is still an abundant amount of snow on the ground when we travel to the cottage. We can get snow well into April and sometimes even in May.

Bru starts to get excited as we pull into the driveway. He knows he will get out soon.

When we get there, we spend a few minutes switching on the fridge and other electrical outlets. My husband cleans out the black stove and takes the old ashes outside to dump in the woods for compost. Then he starts a fire and turns up the heat for each section of floor heating. We usually keep it at a temperature just above freezing so that the porcelain tile and grout doesn't crack due to cold weather.

Besides helping to keep the house warm, the low heat also keeps my plants from freezing. The plants seem to thrive during this kind of hibernation period in the winter and early spring. I've never been good at growing indoor plants, but love them for their greenery and natural aspect. Since I only have to water them when we are here for a weekend, it works for both me and the plants.

We also turn on space heaters, a heated blanket on the bed, and the oven. I usually bake something, while the cottage heats up to a comfortable temperature. It's usually muffins or maybe a pizza. We turn on the television and watch the news or other programs. After a while, we turn everything off, except the floor heat. By morning, it's a comfortable seventy degrees inside again.

Since we have been coming up here, the lake level has drastically varied. We actually have more beach area and less yard, and the lake is closer to the cottage than when we first purchased the vacation home. It's really amazing how the lake levels will change from season to season and even from weekend to weekend.

Bru loves to go outside at the cottage. He runs like a crazy dog, with his ears flopping, up and down the beach area exploring the yard. He has a small squeaky toy that we throw for him to fetch. He will play until we tire of his game.

We love the view each night. Our cottage view reveals St.

Ignace across the lake, a bit of the bridge, the Grand Hotel and other cottages that sit on the south side of Mackinac Island. The island seems closer in the winter. There is not much open water this time of year. The island is about eight miles away, but it seems only a few blocks away. We imagine the quiet and peacefulness of the island, as our cottage has the same tranquil quality.

In the morning, the lake has a spectacular view. The ice that forms near our beach has an artistic draw to it. Our cottage sits on the Lake Huron side of the Straits, and the sunrise is something grand to see over the water and the islands. The water sparkles, and the birds fly in the cloudy skies. The ice makes its own kind of noise as you crunch over it on the beach. Sometimes at night, you can hear it cracking and creaking.

We drive down to the small park by the lake in Mackinaw City. Once the ice starts to melt, shift and move inland, it forms crystals and large ice boulders that are an amazing blue color. Tourists come from all around to see the 'blue ice'. Some people even venture out on the boulders and scramble over them to get to the Mackinac Bridge. And of course, there is an endless amount of people taking selfies by the 'blue ice'.

My husband and I stay closer to the edge of the lake. We scramble up on the boulders that are close to the edge of the water for our selfies. We are very much aware of the dangers of the great lakes, and the ice movement is not safe enough to venture too far out on it.

Another activity that we like to do when we're up north is take a walk on the North Central Rails-to-Trails pathway that is just across the street from the cottage. In the spring, the ice on the trail starts to melt down to a rocky limestone path, and the snowmobilers no longer venture down the trail. The trail and woods perk up with gray and red squirrels, chipmunks, and many varieties of birds.

Bru loves to walk the trail, too. It's peaceful. The trail connects with many other paths, making it great for hiking and biking in the summer and fall. We rarely see others on the trail, during our spring walks.

This year, my husband built three cold frames, which are like smaller greenhouses that sit in the ground and can be used to plant things earlier than usual outside. Two of the cold frames were installed at home, and we brought one up to try at our cottage. We read a book about building them, which was written by someone from northern Maine. We figured if plants could be successfully started in early spring in Maine, then it could be done in northern Michigan as well.

We haven't had a garden in Mackinaw City yet, but we have had good luck with many of the outdoor perennial plants that we grow here, like hostas, day lilies, wild roses, and lily of the valley. We figured we would give a garden a try up here to see what happens. We would start herbs and lettuces in the cold frame, and plan for a small fenced-in garden with other larger vegetables and fruits. We brought fencing leftover from our garden downstate. We planned to till the ground when the weather is nicer and the fear of frost gone. We chose a sunnier patch near the woods in the front yard, as the backyard is quite shady.

The cold frame is near the cottage where some of the perennial plants are located. It's a nice sunny spot near the house and front deck. My husband had to use an ice pick to chop up the ground to get the cold frame leveled. We also ordered automatic greenhouse vents, which are actually made and used in Finland. This will allow venting when the cold frame reaches a certain temperature. That will ensure the plants will not overheat and die.

Once the cold frame was in the ground, I added a large bag of garden compost and also a bag of manure. Horse manure works for the plants on Mackinac Island to nurture all of the many beautiful and robust flowers there. I planted various seeds, like leaf lettuces, arugula, romaine, carrots, radishes, kale, onions and herbs in the cold frame, and labeled them with popsicle sticks from the dollar store. We also planned to add a few veggie plants just outside the deck near the cold frame when the weather gets warmer, including cherry tomatoes, green peppers and wildflowers.

I usually cook something warm and spicy in the crock pot on our weekends, like chicken chili or some other kind of soup. It smells up the cottage nicely. We also run to town to get water in our jugs from the nearest rest area. They leave the outside spigot on for all the brave souls who like to cottage camp like us. We usually go through two five-gallon containers of water for one weekend.

We enjoy our spring visits to the Straits of Mackinac. Springs are cold and peaceful, but we stay warm and cozy in the cottage as we enjoy the ever changing lakeside views and make plans for warmer weather. We keep busy in each season with the different things to do. The summers are even better with the many outdoor sports that we love, like hiking, biking, boating and more. The plants seem to thrive in humid summer weather near the lakes. Bru loves summer weather on the Straits too! With each visit, we hope to make many more memories at the cottage.

Laurie Salisbury

Author and speaker, *Laurie Salisbury*, lives in a rambling old farmhouse in the middle of Michigan. She is a self proclaimed Supermom with the glaring exception of potty training. She has published three children's chapter books in the He Reigns series, *Reins of Love*, *Forever Settled in My Heart*, and *Hope County Fair*. She is currently working on book four, *Rescued Hearts*. Other publications include, *Nothing to Fear*, an infant/toddler picture book based on II Timothy 1:7, and short stories *Twelve Shopping Days* and *Bestest Friend*.

Laurie lives with her beloved husband, Larry, three of her children, Spockie a small rescue dog, and her distinguished feline friend, Dickens. She has spent her life loving and serving children. She raised nine children, gave a temporary home, love, and direction, to twenty-eight foster children, and served in Children's Ministry for over thirty years.

Find out more about Laurie at www.lauriesalisbury.com or join her on Facebook @lauriesalisburyauthor.

Lilacs From a Distance

Rylee had a thing for lilacs. She adored their delicate beauty and gentle grace. The scent of their blooms brought peace to the core of her soul. Years of apartment living had fueled a longing for the fragrant blooms to grace her *own* yard and fill *her* vases.

One sweet day, it happened. Rylee and Mason moved into their dream home in the fall, but Rylee dreamed of spring. Their yard was the biggest on the block, and directly out the dining room window stood a magnificent, gnarled, old lilac bush. For a precious short time in spring, lilacs would bloom on their property. She could pick them to her heart's content. She envisioned filling vases in every room of the house with them.

It took longer to get settled than she had hoped, but by Christmas the house was in order and everything in place. The leaves had long since fallen off the lilac bush. Still, she smiled at its bare branches as she passed the window. The hope of spring warmed in her heart. Christmas passed and the mid-Michigan winter months grew dark and long. January snowstorms led to February freezes. The first sign of melting didn't arrive until the third week of March.

"Don't be fooled," Mason warned, "we'll have an April snow. Just wait."

More snow in April proved him right, but the thaw Rylee had been waiting for soon followed.

Every day she watched the bush for buds. Occasionally, when

it wasn't raining, she would visit the bush and gently run her hands along its branches. At the first sign of the burgeoning blooms, she buried her nose in the bouquets, hoping for a trace of the coming scent.

Despite an unreasonable dread that winter might never end, full bloom arrived in the middle of May. Rylee touched the delicate flowers and filled her nostrils with the tranquilizing scent. She took care to cut stems from all around the bush, leaving plenty to admire from the window as she sipped her morning tea. Just as she'd dreamed, she filled vases and placed them on tables in the main rooms of her home.

Mason, however, had no such dreams. What he had was environmentally-induced asthma and allergies. Rylee was keenly aware of his condition, but not every scent gave him problems. What if this was a scent he *could* tolerate? Surely it wouldn't hurt to test it out on him. How bad could it be?

Several breathing treatments later, he banned the flowers from the house. What could she do? She gathered the lovely blooms and put them in a larger vase on the front porch. At least she could admire them from the picture window and smell them as she passed by each day.

Mason passed the flowers every day too. He grumbled a bit, but Rylee loved his big soft heart for putting up with the momentary nuisance.

She was more than a little surprised at the inner turmoil it caused her, not just a fleeting anger, but feeling crushed at the loss. She reminded herself that she loved her husband more than any flowers, even lilacs. She found it necessary to encourage herself in the Word of God and prayer more times than might otherwise be necessary over such a trivial matter. Why was she so upset about flowers, when the man she loved had such a severe reaction to them? Maybe it was a culmination of the years of unscented laundry soap, or the categorical ban on scented candles, and worst of all, no perfume.

Over the next few months, Rylee prayed that God would change her heart and let her be happy with the lilacs in the yard. Just talking with Him helped her change her focus. *Mason's health is a priority. People, particularly those closest to us, matter ever so much more than plants. My heart will heal in time.*

The blooms disappeared as summer peaked. The bush was lush and green offering the hope of another spring.

Summers were filled with picnics in the yard. Their four young children played around the lovely old bush. A couple of years passed, with Mason suggesting every summer that the old bush be cut back to reduce its monstrous size.

Rylee wouldn't hear of it. "I'll trim it back a bit if you like, but I love it, and I'm not cutting it back to a nub."

One particularly hot summer afternoon, Rylee was in the dining room laying out the noon meal for the kids, when out the window she saw the neighbor cutting down her precious bush. She gasped, and reeled in shock.

"Mason!" She hoped there was still time to save it. "Why is he cutting down my lilac bush?"

"I asked him to," was his calm reply. "It's old and doesn't produce many blooms. Besides, we can't see the kids playing behind it."

In that moment, anger, devastation, and hurt filled her heart. She argued and pleaded, but to no avail. Her lovely bush was scattered all over the lawn.

"I can't wait to move to the new office," said Rylee's co-worker and best friend Tara, as she moved boxes from one side of the small publishing house to the other.

"Um hmm," Rylee said as she stared at her mug of tea.

"You seem out of sorts today," Tara said.

Since Tara noticed the dumpy mood Rylee found herself in, she decided to share the situation with her and vent the anger and frustration. "I can't believe he did it without even talking to me about it."

"Just plant another one somewhere else," Tara said, sliding a black curl from her cheek.

Tara's fix everything approach was great sometimes, but other times it was not what Rylee was wanting to hear. *It would take years for it to bloom and there's no guarantee he'd be okay with me keeping another one. Why can't she just feel sorry for me and buy me ice cream like other best friends?* Rylee slumped at her desk. "I'll have to think about that tomorrow," she said.

As if on cue, Tara scooted out the door.

Rylee woke her desktop computer from its sleepy state and flipped through the day's emails. She stumbled on a personal request for her to edit a piece from someone who had been referred by a friend. Ordinarily, she would quickly transfer the email to her personal account and read it later, but the pretty stationary caught her eye, along with the scripture printed across the top. 'Delight yourself also in the Lord, and He shall give you the desires of your heart. Psalm 37:4.'

She meditated a moment on the words. *My desire is a lilac bush in my backyard. Is that what you will give me?* She had always understood that verse to mean that God would plant a desire — a desire that *He* had, in her heart. Then he would give that desire to her. Not her own desires. But at this moment another scripture came to mind, a verse from the book of John. 'If you ask anything in my name, I will do it.' And, the 'do not worry' passage of Matthew chapter six.

Years of communion with the Father had taught Rylee to recognize the voice of the Lord speaking to her heart. "Both interpretations are correct. I long to give you all that your heart desires. And, yes, I have placed these desires in your heart," He had said. It touched her deeply that the God of the whole universe would care to speak to her.

She bowed her heart and prayed, "Focus my eyes and my heart on you, Lord. Forgive my anger and forgive me for allowing this issue to take my eyes off you. And, thank you. Thank you for caring about the desires of my heart."

Summer was turning to fall, and the more Rylee focused on the Lord and His word, the more the pain lessened in her heart.

"They've delayed the move again." Tara breezed into Rylee's office and plopped in a chair.

"What's up this time?" Rylee asked.

"The deal may have fallen through, something about a technicality in the bid. I'm sick of working around boxes!"

"Ugh," Rylee leaned back and sipped her raspberry tea.

"That's not all," Tara continued. "If this deal falls through, we won't be moving until next year. I can't find anything in this cramped space!"

Rylee traced her finger around the floral design on her mug. "I could write a piece about it." The young copy editor regularly wrote columns for the local newspaper. "It would bring attention to the need and possibly a lead on a bigger, more practical space."

"Ooh, good idea, I'll run it by the big boss. Oh, that reminds me, I have something for you!" Tara's blue eyes sparkled as she jumped from her seat.

Rylee's mouth dropped open when Tara returned with a stubby branch cradled in her arm, the roots wrapped in plastic.

"I can't believe you got me one." She knew even without looking at the package label—it was a lilac bush. Giving was a large part of Tara's nature, and Rylee loved her for it, but this might have stepped over the line. *You can't just insist that someone keep something they don't want, can you?* "I don't know if he'll even let me keep it," she said aloud. Rylee knew this was a decision only Mason could make. He shouldn't have to risk his health for flowers.

"Don't worry about it. You can plant it away from the house and call it a tribute bush in honor of our friendship. He won't say no." Tara had an answer for everything and never seemed to worry about consequences. Admirable qualities at times, but this time Rylee had her doubts.

Not wanting to risk her friendship or her marriage, Rylee decided to accept the gift but talk with Mason before she planted it.

Rylee put the bush on the passenger floorboard and unwound her long dark hair for the ride home. The picture on the package showed lovely lavender blooms. "Lord, I love Mason with all my heart. And I love lilacs. I know that you put both of these loves in my heart. And I know that I am asking for the impossible, but could you please find a way that I can have both? Thank you. I don't have to see the answer to know that you are 'working all these things out for my good', and I love you for that." Just a simple prayer that brought peace to her heart for the ride home.

As she drove past the flat fields of stubble and autumn trees beginning to show their colors, her mind drifted back to two Christmases ago. Mason had bought her a small bottle of perfume. When she opened the gift, he had warned her to use it sparingly.

"I hate when women slather themselves in perfume so that you don't even want to be near them," he said.

"But, how do you know this won't bother you?" Rylee had witnessed the asthma attacks and heard the doctor's warnings.

As if it were the most normal thing in the world, Mason said, "Every time I went to the store, I tested a different perfume on one of those paper strip things. If it gave me an asthma attack, I'd leave the store and do a breathing treatment in the car. If not, I wrote down the name and tested it a few more times. That one never gave me a problem in small doses."

A flood of tears had dropped from Rylee's deep brown eyes that day, and more threatened to fall, even now, as she reminisced about the love of her selfless, generous man.

"It doesn't matter what happens with the silly tribute bush, Lord. I am content with things as they are. Maybe I could give the bush to someone at church if it doesn't work out."

Spring is like a child's whispered wish. It holds promise and hope for something more, something sweet. The tribute bush didn't bloom that next spring, but a flourish of green leaves rustled with promise. It was small, but in Rylee's heart she knew it was strong. It had survived a Michigan winter just inside her property line where Mason had agreed to let her plant it. There would be flowers year after year. For years to come she would watch, now from her kitchen window, for signs of blossoms. She was grateful for lilacs, even from a distance.

Rylee lifted a prayer of gratitude mixed with shame and repentance. "Oh, taste and see that the LORD is good; Blessed is the man who trusts in Him," she quoted from Psalm 34.

Another April came and went. Rylee's news column had done the trick and brought to light an office in the downtown area. It was a charming old building with original oak trim and bare brick walls. The polished wood floors creaked pleasantly as she entered Tara's office.

"I brought you some flowers." Rylee placed the vase on Tara's desk.

"It looks like you have enough for everyone's desk," Tara said, eyeing the crate full of vases. "I can't believe I lost the coin toss for the best office. I'm so jealous."

"I don't know why, I'm sharing the wealth." Rylee smiled and touched the delicate blooms.

Tara smiled and turned back to her work.

Rylee finished her floral deliveries and took the last vase to her desk, a beautiful milk white pitcher full of fragrant blossoms. She leaned over and buried her nose in the dainty flowers before opening her office window. Her heart burst with joy as she gazed over the cobblestone courtyard, surrounded by lilac bushes in full bloom.

IF YOU ENJOYED *SPRING IN THE MITTEN*

YOU ARE SURE TO ENJOY ...

Winter in the Mitten

Find it on Amazon

Made in the USA
Monee, IL
20 November 2021